Electronic systems & techniques

K.F. Ibrahim

Longman Scientific & Technical

To TONIA, DINA and MARK

Longman Scientific & Technical,
Longman Group UK Limited,
Longman House, Burnt Mill, Harlow,
Essex CM20 2JE, England
and Associated Companies throughout the world.

First published 1987

British Library Cataloguing in Publication Data

Ibrahim, K.F.
  Electronic systems and techniques
  1. Electronics
  I. Title
  621.381   TK7815

ISBN 0-582-98817-9

Set in Compugraphic Times 10/12
Produced by Longman Group (FE) limited
Printed in Hong Kong

Contents

Preface

The book may be divided into four parts. Chapters 1–4 provide an introduction to the basic principles of electricity. Chapters 5–18 cover the variety of electronic systems in block diagram (or building block) format starting with the single stage amplifier right across to computer systems. Here the essential knowledge of the relationship between the various blocks or units is established.

Chapters 19–35 look inside the 'building blocks' that make up a system enquiring into their constituent parts and operation. The characteristics of components and the variety of circuitry used in electronics are explained with special attention to modern digital electronics.

Chapters 36 and 37 deal with instruments, testing, and fault finding. Analogue as well as digital measuring devices are included. In fault diagnosis I have employed the functional approach where the state (cut-off or saturation; OFF or ON) of the unit-under-test is examined as the first step to identifying the faulty component.

Although the treatment I have adopted is non-mathematical, the systems and circuits are explained in depth to give the reader a sound understanding in electronics. Wherever possible I have indicated typical values of components that may be found in practice.

The book deals, to one extent or another, with the various aspects of modern electronics. It adequately covers the syllabus of Part I and Part II (core studies) of the City and Guilds 224 Course (Electronic Servicing). A large portion of the C and G 224 Part II Industrial Equipment option is also included. The emphasis on digital electronics is intentional for it is in this field that recent advances have occurred and future developments lay.

Apart from the students taking the City and Guilds 224 Parts I and II examination, this book is suitable for BTEC students at levels I, II and III taking electronic engineering. It is also useful to practising engineers who would like to back their practical background with theoretical knowledge.

It has been my intention throughout the book to meet the

challenge of conveying complex electronic concepts and systems in a manner that may be understood by those who have not had the opportunity of a mathematical background, but who may nonetheless wish to acquire the necessary skills to service modern electronic equipment. To this end I hope I have succeeded.

K.F. Ibrahim

Acknowledgements

We are indebted to the following for permission to reproduce copyright material:

British Standards Institution for our Fig. 17.6; Thorn Consumer Electronics Ltd. for use of information relating to models 1,500, 3,000 and 8,000 T.V. chassis.

1 Direct current

A ———— Electron flow ———— B
–o   o+
Excess of   ←—— Flow of current
electrons

Fig. 1.1 Direct current

Fig. 1.2

(left axis label: Height, equivalent to potential difference)

Tank A

Flow of
water

Tank B

Electric current

All matter consists of very small particles called atoms. These atoms are themselves composed of smaller particles known as **electrons** revolving around a central nucleus composed of one or more **protons** and **neutrons**. The electrons are negative particles while the protons are positive, neutrons are neutral.

If at a point A (Fig. 1.1) there is an excess of electrons as compared with point B, a potential difference (p.d.) or a voltage is said to exist between points A and B. If a conductor such as a wire is now used to connect A to B, the extra electrons at A will begin to flow towards B. This flow of electrons creates an electric current.

Point A with the extra electrons is described as having a negative potential and point B as having a positive potential.

The flow of electrons is similar to the flow of water from tank A to tank B shown in Fig. 1.2. The pipe is equivalent to the electrical conductor while the distance by which tank A is higher than tank B is equivalent to the potential difference between A and B.

Although electrons flow from the negative electrode towards the positive electrode, it is standard practice to say that current flows from positive to negative. This convention dates back to a time before current flow was fully understood. For the purposes of this book, conventional current flow (from positive to negative) will be used.

Potential difference or voltage is measured in volts. Current flow is measured in amperes.

Resistance

Just as a pipe opposes and restricts the flow of water through it, so an electrical resistance opposes and restricts the flow of current between two points. Resistance R is measured in ohms (symbol Ω).

Units

Although the basic units for current, voltage and resistance are the ampere, the volt and the ohm, other units are used which are a fraction or a multiple of the basic unit. These units are shown in Table 1.1.

Table 1.1

	Symbol	Unit
Current	I	ampere A
Voltage	V	volt V
Resistance	R	ohm Ω

milliamp	mA	$= \dfrac{1}{1000}$ A $= 10^{-3}$ A
microamp	μA	$= \dfrac{1}{1000}$ mA $= 10^{-3}$ mA or $\dfrac{1}{1\,000\,000}$ A $= 10^{-6}$ A
millivolt	mV	$= \dfrac{1}{1000}$ V $= 10^{-3}$ V
microvolt	μV	$= \dfrac{1}{1000}$ mV $= 10^{-3}$ mV or $\dfrac{1}{1\,000\,000}$ V $= 10^{-6}$ V
kilovolt	kV	$= 1000$ V $= 10^{3}$ V
kilo-ohm	kΩ	$= 1000\ \Omega = 10^{3}\ \Omega$
mega-ohm	MΩ	$= 1000$ k$\Omega = 10^{3}$ kΩ or $1\,000\,000\ \Omega = 10^{6}\ \Omega$

Ohm's Law

A resistance by definition restricts the flow of current. The quantity of current that a resistor allows through depends on its resistance as well as the potential difference or voltage across it (Fig. 1.3). The greater the resistance, the smaller the current. On the other hand the higher the voltage, the greater the current. This relationship is known as Ohm's Law:

$$\text{Current (amperes)} = \frac{\text{Voltage (volts)}}{\text{Resistance (ohms)}} \quad \text{or} \quad I = \frac{V}{R}$$

Hence, by transposition,

$$R = \frac{V}{I} \quad \text{and} \quad V = IR$$

Fig. 1.3 Resistor in circuit

Resistors in series

R_1 and R_2 are two resistors connected in series (Fig. 1.4(a)). All the current that goes through R_1 must also flow through R_2.

Thus, series resistors have a common current. Their voltages however are different.

EXAMPLE 1

If $R_1 = 2\,\Omega$, $R_2 = 6\,\Omega$, and $I = 3$ A, then

Voltage across R_1 is $V_1 = I \times R_1 = 3 \times 2 = 6$ V and
Voltage across R_2 is $V_2 = I \times R_2 = 3 \times 6 = 18$ V.

The total voltage V between A and B is equal to the sum of the voltages across R_1 and R_2.
Total voltage $V = V_1 + V_2 = 6$ V $+ 18$ V $= 24$ V.

Fig. 1.4 (a) Two resistors in series

Total resistance

R_1 and R_2 can be replaced by a single resistance which gives the same current for the same voltage between points A and B (Fig. 1.4(b)). Such an equivalent resistance is known as the total resistance R_T.

Total resistance $R_T = R_1 + R_2$.

Taking the resistor values of the example above,

$$R_T = R_1 + R_2 = 2 + 6 = 8\,\Omega$$

For a current of 3 A, the voltage can be calculated as

$$V = I \times R_T = 3 \times 8 = 24 \text{ V}.$$

This is the same total voltage as that found by adding V_1 to V_2.

(b) Their equivalent resistance

Three resistors in series

EXAMPLE 2

In Fig. 1.5 $R_1 = 1$ kΩ, $R_2 = 4$ kΩ, $R_3 = 10$ kΩ and battery voltage $V = 15$ V. Calculate the current through the circuit and the voltage across each resistor.

Fig. 1.5 Three resistors in series

Total resistance $R_T = R_1 + R_2 + R_3 = 15$ kΩ

Current $I = \dfrac{\text{Total voltage}}{\text{Total resistance}} = \dfrac{V}{R_T} = \dfrac{15 \text{ V}}{15 \text{ k}\Omega}$

$$= \frac{15 \text{ V}}{15 \times 1000 \text{ }\Omega} = \frac{1}{1000} \text{ A} = 1 \text{ mA}$$

Voltage across R_1: $V_1 = IR_1 = 1 \text{ mA} \times 1 \text{ k}\Omega$

$$= \frac{1}{1000} \text{ A} \times 1000 \text{ }\Omega = 1 \text{ V}$$

Voltage across R_2: $V_2 = IR_2 = 1 \text{ mA} \times 4 \text{ k}\Omega = 4 \text{ V}$
Voltage across R_3: $V_3 = IR_3 = 1 \text{ mA} \times 10 \text{ k}\Omega = 10 \text{ V}.$

The potential divider

Fig. 1.6 The potential divider

As the example above shows, when two or more resistors are connected in series across a d.c. supply, different voltages appear across each resistor. Such an arrangement is called a potential divider and it is used to provide different voltages from a single supply voltage. A simple potential divider is shown in Fig. 1.6 where $R_1 = 2 \text{ k}\Omega$, $R_2 = 1 \text{ k}\Omega$ and supply voltage $V = 30 \text{ V}$. The voltage at point A is the same as the total voltage, 30 V. The voltage at point B, V_B = voltage across R_2.

$$\text{Current through the circuit } I = \frac{\text{Total voltage}}{\text{Total resistance}}$$

$$\frac{30 \text{ V}}{1 \text{ k}\Omega + 2 \text{ k}\Omega} = \frac{30 \text{ V}}{3 \text{ k}\Omega} = \frac{30 \text{ V}}{3000 \text{ }\Omega} = \frac{1}{100} \text{ A}$$

$$= \frac{1}{100} \times 1000 = 10 \text{ mA}$$

Voltage across $R_2 = IR_2 = 10 \text{ mA} \times 1 \text{ k}\Omega$
$$= (10 \times 10^{-3}) \times (1 \times 10^3) = 10 \text{ V}.$$

Another way of calculating the voltage at point B is as follows:

$$V_B = \text{voltage across } R_2 = \frac{\text{Total voltage}}{\text{Total resistance}} \times R_2$$

$$= \frac{V}{R_1 + R_2} \times R_2 = \frac{30 \text{ V}}{2 \text{ k}\Omega + 1 \text{ k}\Omega} \times 1 \text{ k}\Omega = \frac{30}{3} \times 1$$

$$= 10 \text{ V}.$$

This second method applies to any potential divider with two or more resistors in series. The voltage at any point can be calculated in one step using a calculator without the need to find the current first.

Two equal resistors in series

For a potential divider with two equal resistors, the voltage divides equally across them.

Three equal resistors in series

EXAMPLE 3

The potential divider shown in Fig. 1.7 consists of three equal resistors of 1 kΩ each. Calculate the voltage at points A and B relative to E.

$$\text{Total resistance } R_T = R_1 + R_2 + R_3$$
$$= 1 \text{ k}\Omega + 1 \text{ k}\Omega + 1 \text{ k}\Omega = 3 \text{ k}\Omega$$

$$V_{AE} = \text{voltage across } R_1 = \frac{\text{Total voltage}}{\text{Total resistance}} \times R_1$$

$$= \frac{30 \text{ V}}{3 \text{ k}\Omega} \times 1 \text{ k}\Omega = 10 \text{ V}$$

$$V_{BE} = \text{voltage between points B and E}$$

$$= \text{voltage across } (R_1 + R_2) = \frac{30 \text{ V}}{3 \text{ k}\Omega} \times (R_1 + R_2)$$

$$= \frac{30 \text{ V}}{3 \text{ k}\Omega} \times 2 \text{ k}\Omega = 20 \text{ V}.$$

Fig. 1.7 Potential divider using three equal resistors

Potential difference

The potential difference between any two points in a circuit is the difference in their respective voltages (relative to a common point (usually earth)). For instance, the p.d. between A and B in Fig. 1.8 is $V_{AB} = (V_A - V_B)$ where V_A is the voltage at point A and V_B is the voltage at point B. Both V_A and V_B are measured with respect to the zero line E. The voltage at any point in an electric circuit is usually measured with respect to the zero line, chassis or earth.

Fig. 1.8

Fig. 1.9 Voltages considered as heights above and below a datum, the zero line

For example, if V_A is 5 V and V_B is 3 V, $V_{AB} = V_A - V_B = 5 - 3 = 2$ V (see Fig. 1.9(a)).

However, if positive and negative voltages are involved, then the p.d. is the sum of the two voltages. For example, if V_C is 3 V and V_D is -2 V, then $V_{CD} = V_C + V_D = 3 + 2 = 5$ V (Fig. 1.9(b)).

Generally, if the two voltages have the same polarity or sign, the p.d. between them is found by subtracting one from the other. But if the two voltages have different signs, they should be added together.

Resistors in parallel

Fig. 1.10 Two resistors in parallel

Figure 1.10 shows two resistors, R_1 and R_2, connected in parallel. The current I taken from the battery is split at point A into I_1 through R_1 and I_2 through R_2. At B, I_1 and I_2 add up to form the total current I. Thus, total current $I = I_1 + I_2$.

On the other hand, the whole of the total voltage V is applied across each resistor. In other words,

$$\text{Total voltage } V = \text{Voltage across } R_1$$
$$= \text{Voltage across } R_2.$$

Total resistance

The total or equivalent resistance R_T of two resistors in parallel is given by

$$R_T = \frac{R_1 \times R_2}{R_1 + R_2}$$

Note that the total resistance of two resistors in parallel is always **less** than the smaller resistor.

The case of $R_1 = R_2$. The total resistance of two equal resistors in parallel is half the value of one of the resistors.

Three or more resistors in parallel

In general, total resistance of a number of resistors in parallel may be found from the following formula

$$\frac{1}{R_T} = \frac{1}{R_1} + \frac{1}{R_2} + \frac{1}{R_3} \quad \text{and so on}$$

Fig. 1.11

(a)

EXAMPLE 4

For the circuit shown in Fig. 1.11(a) find the total resistance.

(b)

(c)

Fig. 1.11

Solution

R_1 and R_2 are in series, giving a total of $R_{T1} = R_1 + R_2 = 6 + 8 = 14\ \Omega$.

The circuit can now be reduced to that shown in Fig. 1.11(b) with R_{T1} replacing R_1 and R_2 so that R_{T1} is now in parallel with resistor R_3 of an equal value. Their total R_{T2} is half one of them. Therefore the circuit can be further reduced to that shown in (c) with $R_{T2} = 7\ \Omega$ in series with R_4. The total resistance across A and B is therefore $R_{T2} + R_4 = 7 + 3 = 10\ \Omega$.

Power

When current passes through a resistance, energy is lost in the resistor in the form of heat. This is how the electric heater works, by converting electric energy into heat energy.

The unit for electric power is the watt, W. Power P is given by

$$P = V \times I$$

where V is the voltage in volts and I is the current in amps.

Using Ohm's law and substituting for V or I in terms of resistor R, the formula for power can be written as

$$P = I^2 \times R \quad \text{or} \quad P = \frac{V^2}{R} \text{ where } R \text{ is in ohms}$$

Worked examples

EXAMPLE 5

Calculate the voltage across R_3 in Fig. 1.12.

Solution

Total resistance between A and B $= \frac{1}{2} \times 12 = 6\ \Omega$.

Voltage across R_3 = voltage between A and B $= V_{AB} = 4.5$ V.

Fig. 1.12

EXAMPLE 6

Calculate the voltage between X and Y in Fig. 1.13.

Solution

$R_3 + R_4 = 2 + 8 = 10\ \Omega$.

Total resistance between A and Y $= 10/2 = 5\ \Omega$.

Hence, voltage at point A, $V_{AY} = \dfrac{18}{4+5} \times 5 = \dfrac{18}{9} \times 5$

$$= 10 \text{ V}$$

Voltage between X and Y, $V_{XY} = \dfrac{10}{2+8} \times 8 = \dfrac{10}{10} \times 8 = 8$ V

Fig. 1.13

EXAMPLE 7

A 2.5 Ω resistor is connected across a 50 V supply. Calculate the power dissipated.

Solution

The power dissipated in the resistor $= V^2/R = \dfrac{50 \times 50}{2.5}$

$$= 1000 \text{ W} = 1 \text{ kW}$$

EXAMPLE 8

Refer to Fig. 1.14. If the voltage reading at point A is 15 V when switch S is open, what is the reading if the switch is closed?

Solution

When S is closed, the total resistance of the circuit is 0.1 + 4.9 = 5 Ω.

Thus the current through the circuit is 15/5 = 3 A, giving a voltage across the 4.9 Ω load resistor of 3 × 4.9 = 14.7 V, which is the voltage at point A.

Fig. 1.14

2 Alternating current

A direct current flows in one direction only, but an alternating current (a.c.) is a current that continually changes direction.

A battery or a d.c. power supply provides direct current. A signal generator or the public mains supply delivers alternating current.

The sine wave

Alternating current can have many different shapes. These shapes are called waveforms. The most common waveform is the sine wave shown in Fig. 2.1. The sine wave has two equal peaks, a positive peak and a negative peak. The peak value is also known as the amplitude or the maximum value of the sine wave.

The peak-to-peak value of a sine wave is the potential difference between positive peak and the negative peak.

$$\text{Peak-to-peak value} = \text{Positive peak} + \text{Negative peak}$$
$$= 2 \times \text{peak value}$$

Root mean square value

Unlike a direct current which has a constant value that can be used for all calculations, an alternating current varies with time and has no fixed value. To overcome this difficulty, a 'constant' value for the a.c. waveform called the root mean square value (r.m.s.) is used.

The r.m.s. value of an alternating current or voltage is the d.c. equivalent that provides the same power as the original a.c. waveform. Provided the r.m.s. value of an a.c. waveform is known, it can be used in all power calculations just as a d.c. voltage or current. For instance,

$$\text{d.c. power} = \text{d.c. current} \times \text{d.c. voltage}$$
$$\text{a.c. power} = \text{r.m.s. current} \times \text{r.m.s. voltage}$$

Root mean square values are always quoted for a.c. unless otherwise stated.

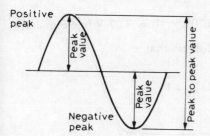

Fig. 2.1 Alternating current

EXAMPLE 1

What is the resistance of a 1 kW domestic heater?

Solution

Domestic heaters use the mains voltage, 240 V r.m.s.
Power dissipated in the heater = 1 kW = 1000 W.

$$\text{From } P = \frac{V^2}{R} \text{ it follows that } R = \frac{V^2}{P} = \frac{240 \times 240}{1000}$$

$$= 57.6\Omega$$

Roots mean square and peak value

The r.m.s. value of an a.c. waveform depends on the shape of the waveform.

For a sine wave, the r.m.s. value = 0.707 × the peak value. This is true *only* for a sine wave.

For a sine wave with a peak voltage V_p of 10 V, its r.m.s. voltage is given by

$$V_{rms} = 0.707 \times V_p = 0.707 \times 10 = 7.07 \text{ V (see Fig. 2.2)}$$

From $V_{rms} = 0.707 \times V_p$ it follows that

$$V_p = \frac{1}{0.707} \times V_{rms} = 1.414 \ V_{rms}$$

Fig. 2.2 The r.m.s. value of a sine wave

Direct current level of a.c. waveforms

So far we have considered a.c. waveforms that have no d.c. level. The two sine waves shown in Fig. 2.3 have the same peak value; sine wave A has a zero d.c. level as it goes positive as much as it goes negative, while sine wave B has a d.c. level of 5 V.

The d.c. level of an a.c. waveform is also referred to as the *average* or the *mean value*.

To find the d.c. level of a rectangular wave. Refer to Fig. 2.4.

1. First establish the zero line.
2. Find the area A_1 above the zero line for one cycle: $A_1 = 4 \times 1 = 4$.

Fig. 2.3 The d.c. level of a.c.

Sine wave A   Sine wave B

Fig. 2.4

3. Find the area A_2 below the zero line for one cycle: $A_2 = 1 \times 2 = 2$.
4. Find the resultant area: $A_1 - A_2 = 4 - 2 = 2$.
5. Average voltage $= \dfrac{\text{Resultant area}}{\text{Periodic time}} = \dfrac{2}{3} = 0.67$ V.

Root mean square for complex waveforms

As stated earlier the formula r.m.s. $= 0.707 \times$ peak is true only for a sinusoidal waveform. Root mean square values for other waveforms may be calculated as follows:

1. Square the waveform over one cycle. Note that squaring a negative value turns it into a positive value.
2. Take the mean of the squared waveform.
3. Take the square root of the mean of the squared waveform, which gives the root mean square.

Hence, using the **square** wave shown in Fig. 2.5a, squaring the positive half cycle gives $3 \times 3 = 9$. Squaring the negative half cycle gives $(-3) \times (-3) = 9$. The average over the squared cycle is therefore 9. Hence the r.m.s. voltage is $\sqrt{9} = 3$ V.

Comparing this with a sine wave having positive and negative peaks of $+3$ V and -3 V respectively, with an r.m.s. of $0.707 \times 3 = 2.12$ V (Fig. 2.5b), we find that the square wave has a higher r.m.s. value than the sine wave. This is because the area under the square waveform is larger than that under the sinusoidal waveform when both are alternating between the same positive and negative values. Note: for a square wave rms value = peak value.

(a)

(b)

Fig. 2.5 Comparison between the r.m.s. values of a square wave and a sine wave

Fig. 2.6   Root mean square for positive-going square wave

Fig. 2.7   (a) The r.m.s. value of a half-wave rectified sine wave is $\frac{1}{2} \times$ peak (b) The r.m.s. value of a full-wave rectified sine wave is $0.7 \times$ peak

Figure 2.6 shows a square wave which is wholly positive. The r.m.s. value is smaller in this case.

For a **rectified** waveform the r.m.s. value may be deduced as follows. For a half-wave rectified sine wave, the r.m.s. value is half the peak value.

For full-wave rectification, the r.m.s. is the same as that for a complete sinusoidal waveform, namely $0.707 \times$ peak value as shown in Fig. 2.7. This is because as far as r.m.s. calculations are concerned, a negative-going half cycle is identical to a positive-going half cycle.

Note that the d.c. or mean value of a waveform is merely the average value over one cycle and thus bears no relation to the r.m.s. value.

3 Waveforms

The variation of a voltage or a current with time can be represented by a waveform.

Direct current being steady, constant current has a straight line waveform (Fig. 3.1(a)). Alternating current on the other hand can have numerous shapes. The a.c. waveform is one which alternates between a maximum value and a minimum value and back to a maximum and so on. They are thus repetitive waveforms (Fig. 3.1(b)). Some such waveforms are shown in Fig. 3.2.

(a)

(b)

Fig. 3.1 (a) d.c. waveform (b) a.c. waveform

A cycle

The part of the a.c. waveform that repeats itself is known as the cycle of the waveform. Referring to Fig. 3.2(a), if we take point A as the beginning of a cycle, then point B will be the end of that cycle and the beginning of the next. The part of the waveform from A to B repeats itself and thus is one cycle.

(a) SINE WAVE

Cycle

(b) SQUARE WAVE

Cycle

(c) RECTANGULAR WAVE

Cycle

(d) TRIANGULAR WAVE

Cycle

(e) SAW TOOTH WAVE

Cycle

(f) PULSE WAVE

Cycle

Fig. 3.2 Types of a.c. waveform

Fig. 3.3 Frequency

Frequency

The number of times a cycle repeats itself in one second is known as the frequency of the waveform. The unit for frequency is the hertz (Hz).

For example, if a waveform repeats itself once every second, its frequency is 1 Hz. If it repeats itself 10 times every second (Fig. 3.3), its frequency is then 10 Hz.

Periodic time

The time taken to complete one cycle is known as the periodic time, or period, of the waveform. For instance, a cycle which takes one second to complete has a periodic time of 1 s. If it takes half a second to complete, its periodic time is 0.5 s.

Mark and Space

One cycle of a rectangular wave can be divided into a Mark and Space as shown in Fig. 3.4. The ratio of Mark time to Space time is known as the Mark-to-Space ratio. If t_1 is the Mark time and t_2 is the Space time then,

$$\text{Mark-to-Space ratio} = \frac{\text{Mark time}}{\text{Space time}} = \frac{t_1}{t_2}$$

The periodic time of the waveform being the time for one complete cycle is

$$\text{Mark} + \text{Space} = t_1 + t_2$$

For a Mark-to-Space ratio of one,

$$\text{Mark time } t_1 = \text{Space time } t_2$$

It follows that

$$\text{Periodic time} = 2 \times \text{Space time} = 2 \times \text{Mark time}$$

The waveform is therefore a square wave.

Fig. 3.4 Mark-to-Space ratio less than one

Units: frequency f

hertz Hz

kilohertz kHz $= 1000 \text{ Hz} = 10^3 \text{ Hz}$

Megahertz MHz $= 1000 \text{ kHz} = 10^3 \text{ kHz} = 10^6 \text{ Hz}$

Units: periodic time T

second s

millisecond ms $= \dfrac{1}{1000} \text{ s} = 10^{-3} \text{ s}$

microsecond μs $= \dfrac{1}{1000} \text{ ms} = 10^{-3} \text{ ms} = 10^{-6} \text{ s}$

Frequency and periodic time

Taking the two waveforms A and B in Fig. 3.5 it can be seen that the frequency of B is double that of A. The periodic time of B on the other hand is half that of A. As the frequency of a waveform increases, so its periodic time decreases and vice versa.

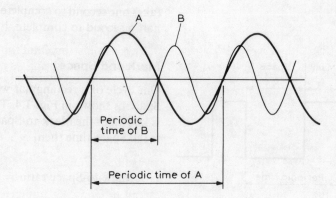

Fig. 3.5

$$\text{Frequency} = \frac{1}{\text{Periodic time}} \text{ Hz} \quad \text{or} \quad f = \frac{1}{T} \text{ Hz and}$$

$$\text{Periodic time} = \frac{1}{\text{Frequency}} \text{ s} \quad \text{or} \quad T = \frac{1}{f} \text{ s}$$

The following table is a useful table of conversion and should be committed to memory.

frequency f	1 Hz	1 kHz	1 MHz
periodic time T	1 s	1 ms	1 μs

Sound waves

Sound waves are those produced in the air when a person is speaking, or from a loudspeaker, a tuning fork, or a pneumatic drill, etc. They are variations of air pressure and require the air as a medium to travel through.

The *volume* of a sound wave indicates its loudness. The *tone* indicates its frequency. By changing the frequency, the tone of the sound is varied.

Audio frequency

The range of sound frequency that can be heard by the human ear is known as the audio frequency (a.f.) range. The a.f. range extends from 20 Hz to 20 kHz. Frequencies below 20 Hz or above 20 kHz cannot be heard by the human ear. This is why the sound produced by special whistles used to call sheep dogs is inaudible by humans. The frequency of these sound waves is above 20 kHz to which the ear of a dog is able to respond.

Pure and instrumental tones

A pure tone is a single sine wave having a single frequency (Fig. 3.2(a)). An instrumental tone is a complex wave composed of a number of different sine waves having different frequencies added together (Fig. 3.1(b)). These are examples of the waveforms produced in speech or music.

Harmonics

By adding a number of different sine waves to one another, a complex wave is produced. Conversely, a complex wave can be found to contain a number of pure sine waves added together. These pure sine waves are known as the fundamental and the harmonics. Any complex waveform can be analysed into the following components:

1. *The fundamental*. A pure sine wave having the same periodic time as the original complex wave.
2. A number of *harmonics*. Pure sine waves having frequencies that are a multiple of the fundamental, e.g. if the fundamental frequency is 100 Hz, then

the 2nd harmonic = 2 × 100 = 200 Hz
the 3rd harmonic = 3 × 100 = 300 Hz
the 4th harmonic = 4 × 100 = 400 Hz and so on.

Higher harmonics have smaller amplitude than the lower ones. For this reason the higher harmonics are usually neglected.

Pitch

The pitch of a sound wave indicates the part of the a.f. range within which its frequency falls. A high-pitched sound falls in the upper half of the a.f. scale while a low-pitched sound falls in the lower half. Women generally have higher pitched voices than men. A drum produces a sound of low pitch while a flute produces high-pitched notes. For a complex wave, the fundamental frequency determines its pitch.

Quality

The quality of sound is determined by the number of harmonics of the instrumental wave that are reproduced without any distortion.

Some complex waves

1. Fundamental + 3rd harmonic only (Fig. 3.6)
2. Fundamental + 2nd harmonic only (Fig. 3.7)

Fig. 3.6 Fundamental + 3rd harmonic (The waveform approximates that of a square wave)

Fig. 3.7 Fundamental + 2nd harmonic (The waveform approximates that of a saw-tooth wave)

The harmonics of a square wave

A square wave consists of the fundamental together with an infinite number of **odd** harmonics only. For example, a square wave having a frequency of 1 kHz contains the following components:

> fundamental = 1 kHz
> 3rd harmonic = 3 × 1 = 3 kHz
> 5th harmonic = 5 × 1 = 5 kHz
> 7th harmonic = 7 × 1 = 7 kHz and so on.

It will be noticed that complex waves containing only odd harmonics have sharp rising and falling edges. The greater the number of these odd harmonics, the nearer we get to a square wave.

The harmonics of a saw-tooth wave

A saw-tooth wave consists of the fundamental together with an infinite number of **even** harmonics only. For example a saw-tooth wave having a frequency of 1 kHz has the following components:

> fundamental = 1 kHz
> 2nd harmonic = 2 × 1 = 2 kHz
> 4th harmonic = 4 × 1 = 4 kHz
> 6th harmonic = 6 × 1 = 6 kHz and so on.

4 Capacitive and inductive networks

Plates

Dielectric

Fig. 4.1 The capacitor

The capacitor

A capacitor consists of two conductor plates facing each other with an insulating material called the **dielectric** separating them (Fig. 4.1). Common dielectric materials are air, paper, mica, etc.

Charging a capacitor

The basic property of a capacitor is its ability to store electric energy in the form of an electric charge.

Figure 4.2(a) shows a battery connected across a capacitor via a switch. When the switch is closed as at (b), the positive electrode of the battery draws electrons from plate A, giving the plate a positive charge. The negative electrode drives electrons to plate B, making it negative by an equal amount. This flow of electrons

(a)

+ Charging Electric
– current field

(b)

Electric
field

(c)

Discharging
current

Load
R

(d)

Fig. 4.2 Charging and discharging a capacitor

is known as the charging current, which continues to flow until the voltage across the capacitor equals the voltage (or electromotive force, e.m.f.) of the battery. The capacitor is then said to be fully charged. The symbol for **charge** is Q and its unit is the Coulomb.

When a capacitor is charged, the potential difference created between the plates produces an electric field.

When the switch is opened as at (c), the capacitor retains the charge within the dielectric which maintains the electric field between its two plates. The electrical field of a charged capacitor will collapse when the capacitor is discharged through a load resistance, as at (d).

Capacitance

The ability of a capacitor to store a charge is known as its capacitance C. The unit of capacitance is the farad F. The farad is a very large unit and therefore hardly used. Smaller units are

$$\text{microfarad } \mu F = \frac{1}{1\,000\,000} \text{ F} = 10^{-6} \text{ F}$$

$$\text{picofarad pF} = \frac{1}{1\,000\,000} \mu F = 10^{-6} \mu F = 10^{-12} \text{ F}$$

Capacitance C increases as the *area* of the plates increases and decreases as the *distance* separating the plates is increased.

For example, if the area of the plates is doubled the capacitance will double in value. However, if the distance is doubled, the capacitance is halved.

Charge, capacitance and voltage

When a capacitor is charged to a voltage V, the charge Q is given by

$$Q = C \times V$$

where C is in farads, V in volts, and Q in coulombs.

$$\text{By transposition } C = \frac{Q}{V} \quad \text{and} \quad V = \frac{Q}{C}$$

Energy

The energy stored by a capacitor is given by

$$\text{Energy } W = \tfrac{1}{2}CV^2$$

where W is in joules, C is in farads, and V is in volts.

Capacitors in parallel and series

When two capacitors C_1 and C_2 are connected in parallel (Fig. 4.3(a)) their total capacitance is the sum of the two capacitances, i.e.

Total capacitance $C_T = C_1 + C_2$

When connected in series (Fig. 4.3(b)) the total is smaller than either one:

Total capacitance $C_T = \dfrac{C_1 C_2}{C_1 + C_2}$

For example, if $C_1 = C_2$, their total when connected in series is half one of them; $\frac{1}{2}C_1 = \frac{1}{2}C_2$.

Fig. 4.3 (a) Capacitors in parallel (b) Capacitors in series

(a)   (b)

Voltage across series capacitors

In the circuit shown in Fig. 4.4, C_1 is in series with C_2 with a d.c. voltage V_T connected across them. The total voltage V_T will divide between C_1 and C_2 so that the smaller capacitor will sustain a higher voltage across it and vice versa. The sum of V_1 (across C_1) and V_2 (across C_2) is always equal to the total voltage V_T.

Fig. 4.4 Voltage across series capacitors

Total voltage $V_T = V_1 + V_2$ with $\dfrac{V_1}{V_2} = \dfrac{C_2}{C_1}$

In general, when a number of capacitors are connected in series across a d.c. supply, the voltage across each capacitor is inversely proportional to its capacitance. For two capacitors in series (Fig. 4.4) the voltage across C_1 and C_2 are given as

$$V_1 = \frac{V_T}{C_1 + C_2} \times C_2; \quad V_2 = \frac{V_T}{C_1 + C_2} \times C_1$$

Fig. 4.5

EXAMPLE 1

In Fig. 4.5 the total capacitance is calculated as follows. Total capacitance of parallel combination is

Fig. 4.6

Fig. 4.7

Fig. 4.8

Fig. 4.9

$C_2 + C_3 = 10 + 20 = 30$ pF

Since C_1 is also 30 pF, then the total capacitance is $\frac{1}{2} \times 30 = 15$ pF.

EXAMPLE 2

In Fig. 4.6 the voltage across capacitor C_1 is

$$\frac{V_T}{C_1 + C_2} \times C_2 = \frac{30}{0.1 + 0.2} \times 0.2 = 20 \text{ V}$$

giving a voltage across $C_2 = 30 - 20 = 10$ V.

Working voltage

Every capacitor has a maximum voltage it can sustain before the dielectric breaks down. This voltage is known as the working voltage of the capacitor and it must never be exceeded. When used in a.c. applications, the peak voltage applied across the capacitor must not exceed the specified working voltage of the capacitor. The working voltage of a number of capacitors connected in parallel is that of the capacitor with the lowest working voltage. For example in Fig. 4.7, the working voltage of the parallel circuit is 25 V.

For capacitors in series the working voltage is more difficult to work out. Consider the circuit in Fig. 4.8 where C_1 (1 μF, working voltage WV = 25 V) is in series with C_2 (10 μF, WV = 10 V). Since the smaller capacitor C_1 will sustain a higher voltage than C_2, then start the calculations with C_1 at its specified working voltage of 25 V. Thus $V_1 = 25$ V. But $V_2/V_1 = C_1/C_2$, so

$$V_2 = V_1 \times \frac{C_1}{C_2} = 25 \text{ V} \times \frac{1 \text{ μF}}{10 \text{ μF}} = 2.5 \text{ V}$$

Since V_2 is below the working voltage of C_2, then the overall working voltage is $25 + 2.5 = 27.5$ V.

However, if C_2 had a working voltage of say 2 V as in Fig. 4.9, it will reach its working voltage before C_1 voltage reaches 25 V. The overall working voltage is calculated as follows:

$$V_2 = 2 \text{ V and } V_1 = V_2 \times \frac{C_2}{C_1} = 2 \times \frac{10}{1} = 20 \text{ V}$$

giving an overall working voltage of $20 + 2 = 22$ V.

EXAMPLE 3

Refer to Fig. 4.10 with C_1 and C_2 having the same working voltage of 60 V. What is the maximum voltage that may be applied?

Fig. 4.10

Fig. 4.11 Simple inductor

Fig. 4.12 The inductor

Fig. 4.13

(a)

(b)

Fig. 4.14 Charging and discharging curves, where t is the time constant

Solution

Since C_1 sustains a higher voltage across it than C_2, the former will reach its working voltage first.

with $V_1 = 60$ V,

$$V_2 = \frac{C_1}{C_2} \times V_1 = \frac{2}{6} \times 60 = 20 \text{ V}$$

The maximum voltage that may be applied $= 60 + 20 = 80$ V.

The inductor

The inductor is simply a conductor wound as shown in Fig. 4.11. Its symbol is shown in Fig. 4.12. While a capacitor opposes a change of voltage across it, an inductor opposes a change of current through it. In other words if a step current is applied to a circuit with an inductor, current will slowly build up to its maximum.

This ability of an inductor to oppose a change in current is known as its inductance. The symbol of inductance is L and its unit is the Henry H. In smaller units,

$$\text{milli-Henry mH} = \frac{1}{1000} \text{ H} = 10^{-3} \text{ H}$$

$$\text{micro-Henry } \mu\text{H} = \frac{1}{1000} \text{ mH} = 10^{-3} \text{ mH} = \frac{1}{1\,000\,000} \text{ H}$$

$$= 10^{-6} \text{ H}$$

Time constant for CR circuit

Figure 4.13 shows a capacitor in series with a resistor connected across a battery via a switch. When the switch is in position (1), the capacitor gradually charges up through resistor R until the voltage across it is equal to E, the e.m.f. or voltage of the battery.

The manner in which the capacitor charges up is shown in Fig. 4.14(a) along an exponential curve.

The time taken for the capacitor to charge to 0.63 of the maximum, in this case 0.63 E, is known as the time constant of the circuit.

Referring back to Fig. 4.11, if the switch is now moved to position (2), the capacitor will store the energy, keeping the voltage across it constant. When the switch is moved to position (3), the capacitor begins to discharge through resistor R to earth. The voltage across the capacitor gradually falls to zero. The manner in which the discharge takes place is shown in Fig. 4.12(b). In this case the time constant is the time it takes the voltage across the capacitor to fall by 0.63 of its maximum value.

For either charging or discharging a capacitor through a resistor R, the time constant is given by

$$t = C \times R$$

where t is the time constant in seconds, C is the capacitance in farads, R is the resistance in ohms.

For example if $C = 10 \mu F$ and $R = 10 k\Omega$ then the time constant of the circuit is

$$t = CR = 10 \mu F \times 10 k\Omega = 10 \times 10^{-6} \times 10 \times 10^3$$
$$= 10 \times 10 \times 10^{-3} = 10^2 \times 10^{-3} = 10^{-1} = 0.1 \text{ s.}$$

Figure 4.15 shows charging curves for a short and a long time constant.

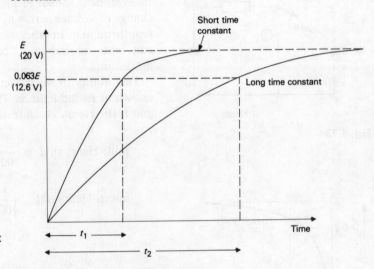

Fig. 4.15 Changing curves for a short and a long time constant

Time constant for an LR circuit

Consider the circuit in Fig. 4.16 with inductor L in series with a 1 kΩ resistor R. When switch S closes the current is zero, attempting to increase sharply. However, since the inductor opposes any change of current through it, the current I through the circuit will increase exponentially, as shown in Fig. 4.17. The current will continue to increase until it reaches it maximum value. At this point the current stops increasing, with the whole applied voltage E falling across R. Steady-state current

$$= E/R = 20/1 k\Omega = 20 \text{ mA}$$

The rate of change of current is dependent upon the values of both R and L.

The time it takes the current to reach 0.63 of its maximum steady state is known as the time constant of the circuit. This may be calculated as L/R, where L is in Henries and R is in ohms, and the time constant is in seconds. Using the values in the diagram,

Fig. 4.16

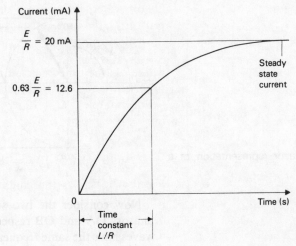

Fig. 4.17 Exponential increase of a current through an inductor

$$\text{time constant} = \frac{L}{R} = \frac{100 \text{ mH}}{1 \text{ k}\Omega} = \frac{0.1 \text{ H}}{1000 \text{ }\Omega}$$

$$= 10^{-4} \text{ s} = 0.1 \text{ ms}$$

Note that for a large R, the time constant L/R is small, with the current changing at a faster rate.

Direct current resistance

An inductor presents no resistance to the flow of d.c. current other than the very small resistance of the wire from which it is made. Thus an inductor has zero or very small d.c. resistance and can be considered as a short circuit for d.c. A capacitor on the other hand, due to the insulating dielectric, presents an infinite or very large resistance to direct current and can be considered as an open circuit for d.c.

Phasor representation

A sine wave may be represented by a phasor OA rotating anti-clockwise at an angular velocity $\omega = 2\pi f$, where f is the frequency of the waveform (Fig. 4.18). As the phasor rotates, the height of its tip (point A) above the horizontal axis describes the sine wave shown. One complete revolution of the phasor (360° or 2π) represents one complete cycle. Thus half a revolution (180° of π) represents half a cycle, and so on. The time axis of the waveform may, therefore, be used to represent the angle through which the phasor has moved, as shown in the figure. The positive peak value is therefore at 90° ($\frac{1}{4}$ cycle) and the negative peak is at 270° ($\frac{3}{4}$ cycle).

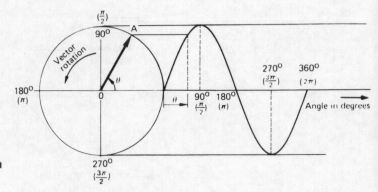

Fig. 4.18   Phasor representation of a sine wave

Now consider the two sine waves A and B, represented by phasors OA and OB respectively, in Fig. 4.19(a). If both sine waves have the same frequency, then both OA and OB will rotate at equal angular velocity $\omega = 2\pi f$. This means that the angular difference θ between OA and OB does not change. OA is said to be *leading* OB by an angle of θ, or OB is *lagging* OA by an angle of θ. The sine waves are as shown in Fig. 4.19(b).

If these two sine waves are added together, their resultant will be another sine wave having the same frequency f but a different amplitude. The resultant sine wave may be represented by a separate phasor OT which is the phasor sum of OA and OB as shown in Fig. 4.19(c). The resultant waveform leads OB by angle α and lags OA by angle γ.

Fig. 4.19   Phase difference. OA leads OB (or OB lags OA) by angle θ

As we shall see in the remainder of this chapter, phasor representation is a very useful device in analysis and calculation in a.c. networks.

Phase difference

When a voltage V is applied across a resistor R a current I flows through it. The voltage and current are distinct electrical qualities with their own units and waveforms.

In the case of d.c. networks (Chapter 1) the question of waveforms does not arise. For a.c. networks the relationship between the current and voltage waveforms is very important. For a resistor R the voltage across it is in phase with the current through it, i.e. the phase difference is zero as shown in Fig. 4.20(b) and (c).

Fig. 4.20

When an alternating voltage is applied across an inductor (Fig. 4.21) a 90° phase difference is introduced between the voltage and current, with the voltage *leading* the current.

When an alternating voltage is applied across a capacitor a similar phase difference of 90° is introduced between the voltage and current waveforms, but in this case the voltage will be *lagging* the current as shown in Fig. 4.22.

Fig. 4.21

a.c. input

Fig. 4.22

(a)

(b)

Fig. 4.23 (a) *LR* circuit for Example 1 (b) Phasor diagram

EXAMPLE 1

For the *LR* circuit shown in Fig. 4.23(a) draw the phasor diagram, and hence find the total applied voltage V_T.

Solution

The phasor diagram is as shown in Fig. 4.23(b). The phasor representing the current I is drawn first. V_R is then drawn in phase with I and V_L leading the current (and hence V_R) by 90°. The total applied voltage V_T is the phasor sum of V_R and V_L produced as shown. If the phasor diagram is drawn to scale, V_T may be found to be 7 V. As can be seen, the total applied voltage is leading the current by an angle $\theta = 45°$. Note that the total applied voltage is greater than either of the two component voltages (V_R and V_L) but smaller than their arithmetical sum.

EXAMPLE 2

For the *RC* series circuit shown in Fig. 4.24(a) draw the phasor diagram and find the applied voltage.

Solution

The phasor diagram is as shown in Fig. 4.24(b) with V_C lagging the current (and V_R) by 90°. V_T is the phasor sum of V_R and V_C. From the diagram, V_T is greater than either component voltage, i.e. greater than 4 V but smaller than their arithmetical sum (smaller than $3 + 4 = 7$ V). If the phasor diagram is drawn to scale, V_T may be found to be 5 V, lagging the current by angle $\alpha = 36°$.

V_T
Applied
voltage

Fig. 4.24

(a)

EXAMPLE 3

For the *LRC* circuit shown in Fig. 4.25(a) draw the complete phasor diagram and hence find the total voltage.

Fig. 4.25 (a) *LRC* circuit for Example 3 (b) Phasor diagram (c) Resultant phasor

Solution

The phasor diagram is as shown in Fig. 4.25(b), with V_R in phase with current I, V_L leading by 90° and V_C lagging by 90°. Since V_L and V_C fall along the same vertical line they may be reduced to the single phasor

$$OZ = V_L - V_C = 90 - 60 = 30 \text{ V}$$

as shown in Fig. 4.25(c). The total voltage V_T is, therefore, the phasor sum of V_R and OZ. $V_T = 50$ V leading the current by angle $\alpha = 36°$.

Reactance

Inductors and capacitors offer opposition to the flow of alternating current. This a.c. resistance is known as reactance X and is measured in ohms. Reactance depends on the value of the inductor or the capacitor as well as the frequency of the a.c. waveform.

An inductor has an inductive reactance X_L,

$$X_L = 2\pi f L$$

where f is the frequency in Hz and L is the inductance in henries.

Since $\omega = 2\pi f$, then $X_L = \omega L$. For example a 10 mH inductor fed with a 1 kHz signal has a reactance

$$X_L = 2\pi \times 1 \times 10^3 \times 10 \times 10^{-3} = 2\pi \times 10 = 62.8 \ \Omega$$

The reactance of an inductor increases with frequency (Fig. 4.26).

A capacitor has a capacitive reactance X_C,

Fig. 4.26 Graph showing how the reactance of an inductor X_L changes with frequency

Fig. 4.27

$$X_C = \frac{1}{2\pi f C} = \frac{1}{\omega C}$$

where C is the capacitance in farads. A 1 µF capacitor, for example, operating at 10 kHz has a reactance

$$X_C = \frac{1}{2\pi \times 10 \times 10^3 \times 1 \times 10^{-6}} = \frac{1}{2\pi \times 10^{-2}}$$

$$= \frac{10^2}{2\pi} = 15.9 \ \Omega$$

The reactance of a capacitor decreases with increasing frequency (Fig. 4.27)

A network consisting of a capacitive reactance X_C and an inductive reactance X_L has a total reactance given by the phasor sum of X_C and X_L. The two vectors X_C and X_L are in anti-phase as shown in Fig. 4.28(b), i.e. they have a phase difference of 180°. Hence the total reactance is simply the difference between the values of X_C and X_L. For example, given that $X_L = 100 \ \Omega$ and $X_C = 70 \ \Omega$, then the total reactance $X = 100 - 70 = 30 \ \Omega$ which is inductive since X_L is greater than X_C.

Fig. 4.28 Phasor sum of a capacitive X_C and an inductive X_L reactance

Impedance

A network consisting of a reactance (inductive or capacitive) and a resistance has a total a.c. resistance known as its impedance Z. The impedance Z is the phasor sum of reactance X and resistance R.

For example, consider the reactive inductance X_L in series with resistor R in Fig. 4.29. As shown in 4.29(b), phasor X_L leads phasor R by 90° giving

Impedance $Z = \sqrt{(X_L^2 + R^2)}$

For $X_L = 400 \ \Omega = 4 \times 10^2 \ \Omega$ and $R = 300 \ \Omega = 3 \times 10^2 \ \Omega$,

$$Z = \sqrt{(16 \times 10^4 + 9 \times 10^4)} = \sqrt{(25 \times 10^4)} = (5 \times 10^2)$$
$$= 500 \ \Omega$$

Fig. 4.29 (a) Inductor L in series with resistor R (b) Phasor representation of R, X_L and their phasor sum Z

5 Amplifiers and oscillators

Amplifiers are very widely used devices in many types of electronic systems. They have the property of amplification, i.e. the process of producing an output larger than the original input.

Gain

The gain of an amplifier is the number of times its output is bigger than its input.

$$\text{Gain} = \frac{\text{Output}}{\text{Input}} \text{ and has no units } - \text{ it is merely a ratio.}$$

There are three kinds of gain:

$$\text{Voltage gain } G_v = \frac{\text{Output voltage}}{\text{Input voltage}} = \frac{V_0}{V_{in}} \text{ (no units)}$$

$$\text{Current gain } G_i = \frac{\text{Output current}}{\text{Input current}} = \frac{I_0}{I_{in}} \text{ (no units)}$$

$$\text{Power gain } G_p = \frac{\text{Output power}}{\text{Input power}} = \frac{P_0}{P_{in}} \text{ (no units)}$$

Gain of two or more stages

A 2-stage amplifier is as shown in Fig. 5.1.

The output V_1 from the first stage is fed into the second stage. Thus V_1 becomes the input to the second stage. The overall input

Fig. 5.1 Gain of two stages $= G_1 \times G_2$

is V_{in} and the overall output is V_0. The overall gain G of the amplifier is given as

$$G = \frac{\text{Overall output}}{\text{Overall input}} = \frac{V_0}{V_{in}}$$

Assuming the gain of the first stage G_1 is 20 and that of the second stage G_2 is 50, then if the input voltage, V_{in} was 1 mV,

$$V_1 = \text{gain of the 1st stage} \times V_{in} = 20 \times 1\ mV = 20\ mV$$
$$V_0 = \text{gain of the 2nd stage} \times V_1 = 50 \times 20\ \text{mV}$$
$$= 1000\ \text{mV} = 1\ \text{V}$$

$$\text{Overall gain } G = \frac{V_0}{V_{in}} = \frac{1000\ \text{mV}}{1\ \text{mV}} = 1000$$

The overall gain of the amplifier can more easily be calculated as

$$G = \text{Gain of first stage} \times \text{gain of second stage}$$
$$= G_1 \times G_2 = 20 \times 50 = 1000$$

Similarly, the gain of a 3-stage amplifier is given by

$$G = G_1 \times G_2 \times G_3$$

and so on for any number of stages.

Frequency response

The frequency response curve of an amplifier shows how the gain or the output of the amplifier changes with the signal frequency.

The frequency response curve (Fig. 5.2) is the graph of voltage output (or gain) on the y-axis against frequency on the x-axis. A logarithmic (non-linear) scale is used for the frequency − this spreads out the low-frequency end and compresses the high-frequency end.

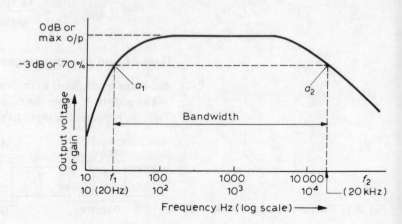

Fig. 5.2 Frequency response curve

The output (and the gain) of the amplifier is constant at the mid-frequency range but falls at high and low frequencies. The range of frequencies between f_1 and f_2 is the bandwidth of the amplifier. f_1 and f_2 correspond to points a_1 and a_2 on the curve known as the 3 dB (decibel) points. The decibel is a non-linear (logarithmic) unit for measuring gain (see Appendix II). Point a_1 is known as the lower 3 dB point while a_2 is known as the upper 3 dB point. These two points are chosen where the voltage output of the amplifier has fallen to 70% of its maximum value. The 3 dB points are also known as the half-power points since the output power of the amplifier at the corresponding two frequencies is half its maximum value.

The output voltage (or the gain) on the y-axis can be represented in decibels, the maximum as 0 dB and the level for the 3 dB points as -3 dB.

The a.f. response curve

In order to amplify all audio frequencies the a.f. amplifier must have a bandwidth equivalent to the a.f. range, i.e. from 20 Hz to 20 kHz. Along this range of frequencies the gain of the amplifier should be steady. Below 20 Hz and above 20 kHz, the gain falls. Figure 5.2 shows a typical a.f. response curve.

As music and speech contain a complex mixture of frequencies within the a.f. band, the quality of an amplifier depends on how many of these frequencies and their harmonics it can reproduce without distortion. A small bandwidth will necessarily restrict the number of harmonics that can be reproduced at the output, hence the low quality of sound produced by cheap amplifiers.

There are two main types of distortion: amplitude and frequency.

Amplitude—amplitude distortion

Every amplifier has a maximum output that it cannot exceed. Once exceeded, the output will suffer from amplitude distortion. This is shown by the flattening or cutting off of one or both peaks of the waveform.

Figure 5.3 shows three ways in which a sine wave input can suffer amplitude distortion at the output of an overdriven amplifier.

Alternation—frequency distortion

Amplifiers are required to reproduce the input waveform without any change in its shape apart from an increase in its amplitude. Usually, the input signal is a complex wave consisting of a number of sine waves of different frequencies and their harmonics. For a faithful reproduction, all these frequencies must be

Fig. 5.3 Amplitude distortion

amplified by the same ratio. That is to say the gain of the amplifier must be the same for all of them. In other words, the frequency response curve of the amplifier must be reasonably flat over the whole bandwidth, otherwise the output will suffer from frequency distortion.

For example, an amplifier with the response curve shown in Fig. 5.4 will have the high frequencies amplified more than the lower frequencies. The output will contain an over-emphasis of high frequencies. The output is then said to suffer from frequency distortion.

Fig. 5.4

Voltage amplifiers

These are the most commonly used amplifiers. They have a large voltage gain to provide maximum voltage at the output. They are used whenever a large voltage swing is required, e.g. in a driver stage to drive the power amplifier.

Power amplifiers

These have a large power and current gain to produce maximum power output. A power amplifier is used as the final stage in an electronic system to drive the power into the load. Typical values of output power requirements of commonly used systems are:

small radio amplifier	200 mW
hi fi	10 W
public address system	100 W or more

Push−pull amplifier

In order to get a high power output from an amplifier with less amplitude distortion, a push−pull power amplifier is used (Fig. 5.5).

Fig. 5.5 Push–pull amplifier

Fig. 5.6 Cross-over distortion

In the push–pull amplifier, the signal is first fed into a phase splitter which splits the waveform into two halves: a positive half and a negative half. Each half is then amplified by a separate amplifier, amplifier A_1 for the positive half and amplifier A_2 for the negative half. Once amplified, the two halves are added together by the mixer or output unit to reproduce the complete cycle which is fed into the loudspeaker load.

The output of the push–pull amplifier suffers from a distortion in the waveform known as cross-over distortion shown in Fig. 5.6. Cross-over distortion is easily overcome by proper design of the circuit.

Wide-band amplifier

A wide-band amplifier has a large bandwidth starting at practically zero Hz (d.c.) up to a few MHz. The wide bandwidth is achieved at the expense of the gain. Compared with the a.f. amplifier, the wide-band amplifier has a much larger bandwidth but a lower gain.

Wide-band amplifiers are used in TV receivers and for pulse amplification where a large band of frequencies is present – up to 5 MHz or more (Fig. 5.7). These amplifiers are also known as video amplifiers. Other uses are in radar and as Y-amplifiers for oscilloscopes.

A wide-band amplifier is also used for a complex wave with a large number of harmonics. The greater the number of harmonics present, the wider the bandwidth of the amplifier must be, otherwise distortion occurs. For a square wave with an infinite number of harmonics, the bandwidth required is also infinite. However, in practice the higher harmonics, the ninth or

Fig. 5.7 Wide-band video amplifier

eleventh onwards, being small in amplitude, are neglected without much damage to the waveform.

Radio frequency amplifiers

Radio frequency amplifiers are used in radio transmitters and receivers. They are selective amplifiers tuned to one particular radio frequency, and may have a very narrow bandwidth and a very high gain.

A typical response curve is shown in Fig. 5.8. It shows the narrow bandwidth between the two 3 dB points. f_0 is the tuning frequency of the amplifier. When tuned to a different frequency f_0', the response curve shifts along to the position shown by a dotted line.

Fig. 5.8   R.F. amplifier response curve

Feedback

Feedback is the process of feeding part or all of the output of an amplifier back to the input (Fig. 5.9). There are two types of feedback: positive and negative.

Fig. 5.9   Feedback

Positive feedback

Feedback is known as positive when the signal fed back is in the same phase as the original input. The effect of positive feedback is to *increase* the gain of the amplifier (leading to instability and possible oscillation) and to reduce the bandwidth.

Negative feedback

Feedback is known as negative when the signal fed back is in opposition to the original input. Contrary to positive feedback, this kind of feedback *reduces* gain, improves stability and increases the bandwidth of the amplifier. The effect of negative feedback on the response curve is to make it steadier and flatter as shown in Fig. 5.10.

Fig. 5.10 Effect of feedback on the frequency response curve

Oscillators

These are amplifiers with such a large amount of positive feedback that an output is produced without any 'external' input (Fig. 5.11). The level of the output is determined by the gain of the amplifier as well as the feedback network.

As explained in Chapter 32 sine wave oscillators are tuned circuits to select the frequency of oscillation. The frequency of oscillation can be changed by changing the component values of the tuned circuit.

Square wave oscillators use no tuned circuits. Instead an *RC* feedback network is used, e.g. as in a multivibrator. The shape, i.e. the mark-to-space ratio, and the frequency of the square wave are determined by the values of *R* and *C* used.

One important requirement of an oscillator is that its frequency should remain constant while it is in use. Changes in the frequency of oscillation occur for two reasons. First, temperature change may cause component values to drift, and these changes produce **frequency drift**. Frequency drift can be overcome by the use of compensatory circuits to counterbalance these changes keeping the frequency constant at all temperatures, or keeping the frequency determining units in a constant temperature oven.

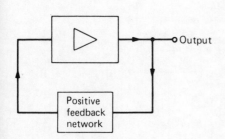

Fig. 5.11 The oscillator

Second, change may occur due to variable loading of the oscillator. This is known as **frequency pulling**. To prevent this happening, a buffer stage is used to isolate the oscillator from the load. The load could be a loudspeaker or an amplifier stage (as shown in Fig. 5.12). The buffer stage presents the correct load to the oscillator no matter what the final load is.

Fig. 5.12   The use of a buffer stage

Audio frequency signal generator (Fig. 5.13)

Fig. 5.13   A.F. signal generator

The a.f. oscillator generates the signal and determines its frequency. The signal is amplified by the voltage amplifier to give the necessary voltage swing needed to drive the output stage. The output stage is a power amplifier which drives the power into the load. The a.f. oscillator, voltage amplifier and the power output stage are fed with the necessary d.c. power from the d.c. power supply.

Before feeding the signal into the load, it goes into the attenuator. The attenuator is a passive network (hence no d.c. supply) which controls the level of the output signal. It contains (*a*) a step attentuator giving control in steps of 20 dB, i.e. by a factor of 10, and (*b*) a continuous attenuator giving continuous and fine control of the output level.

6 Resonance

Fig. 6.1 Series resonance

Fig. 6.2 Response curve for a series resonant circuit

Fig. 6.3 Parallel resonance

Series resonance

Consider the series network in Fig. 6.1 with resistor R in series with inductor L and capacitor C. Resistor R may be an actual resistor or may represent the resistance of the inductor. The value of R is independent of frequency and stays constant at all frequencies. The reactances of L and C, on the other hand, are frequency-dependent. Thus as the frequency is increased from d.c. (zero Hz), the reactance of L increases while that of C decreases until at one frequence f_0, the reactances X_L and X_C become equal. At this point the circuit is said to be at resonance, with f_0 as the frequency of resonance.

Being in anti-phase to each other X_L and X_C cancel each other, resulting in a purely resistive impedance $Z = R$. With Z at this minimum value, the current through the circuit is at maximum, giving the response curve shown in Fig. 6.2. Because a series resonant circuit has a maximum current at resonance, it is also known as an **acceptor** circuit.

Parallel resonance

Resonance may be obtained with the parallel circuit shown in Fig. 6.3. At one specified frequency determined by the values of L and C the reactance of L cancels that of C and produces resonance. The impedance is now at a maximum giving maximum voltage. The circuit is thus known as a **rejector**, with a frequency response shown in Fig. 6.4.

For both series and parallel resonance, the resonant frequency is given as

$$f_0 = \frac{1}{2\pi\sqrt{(LC)}}$$

Given that $L = 10$ mH and $C = 1\mu$F then

$$f_0 = \frac{1}{2\pi \times \sqrt{(10 \times 10^{-3} \times 1 \times 10^{-6})}}$$

39

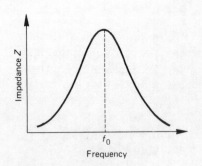

Fig. 6.4 Response curve for a parallel resonant circuit

$$= \frac{1}{2\pi\sqrt{10^{-8}}} = \frac{1}{2\pi \times 10^{-4}} = \frac{10^4}{2\pi} = 1.59 \text{ kHz}$$

Note that the value of the resistance in the circuit does not affect the frequency at which the resonance occurs.

Bandwidth and selectivity

Resonant circuits are used mainly as tuned circuits because of their selective frequency response. Normally, parallel tuned circuits are used since they have a high impedance and thus a high voltage output.

The frequency response of a tuned circuit is shown in Fig. 6.5.

Fig. 6.5 Frequency response curve for a tuned circuit. Δf is the bandwidth

The bandwidth is taken between the 3 dB points as shown. The selectivity of a tuned circuit is a measure of its ability to reject adjacent frequencies in favour of the required tuned frequency. A more selective circuit has a narrower bandwidth compared with a less selective circuit having a wider bandwidth. Selectivity is measured by its Q-factor which is defined as

$$\text{Q-factor} = \frac{\text{Resonant frequency}}{\text{Bandwidth}} = \frac{f_0}{\Delta f} \text{ (Fig. 6.5)}$$

Hence a highly selective circuit has a high Q-factor; a less selective circuit has a low Q-factor.

Damping

Where a wide bandwidth is required, say for a TV receiver, low-Q tuned circuits are needed. The low Q-factor may be achieved by shunting the tuned circuit with a resistor R as shown in Fig. 6.6(a). The resistor has what is known as a damping effect on the response curve, making the circuit less selective, as shown in 6.6(b).

Fig. 6.6 Damping effect on a tuned circuit

Damped oscillation

Consider a resonant circuit tuned to a frequency of 1 kHz. Since the circuit rejects all other frequencies, the only output that may appear across it will be in the form of a 1 kHz sine wave. Such an output may be produced by feeding the circuit with a.c. energy which makes it oscillate sinusoidally. This a.c. energy may be in the form of a sine wave at the resonant frequency or a complex waveform having a harmonic at the resonant frequency.

Figure 6.7 shows a resonant circuit tuned to 3 kHz fed with a 1 kHz square wave. The tuned circuit will oscillate to the third harmonic of the square wave (i.e. 3 kHz) producing sustained oscillations as shown. Figure 6.8 shows the same tuned circuit, this time fed with a step voltage generated by closing switch S.

Fig. 6.7 A tuned circuit oscillating at the third harmonic of the input

Fig. 6.8 Damped oscillation produced by a tuned circuit fed with a step waveform

The step voltage contains an infinite number of harmonics which energises the tuned circuit into oscillating at its 3 kHz resonant frequency. However, the oscillations are damped, i.e. dying out, since the a.c. energy produced by the step voltage is gradually lost due to the small losses in L and C as well as in the resistance of the connecting wires, etc. After a while the oscillations stop completely. Another set of damped oscillations may be produced by opening switch S.

Damped oscillation occurs whenever the energy fed into the resonant circuit is not high enough or frequent enough to overcome the losses in the circuit.

7 Transformers

Fig. 7.1 Magnetic field due to current

Fig. 7.2 (a) Current coming out (b) Current going in

Fig. 7.3 Magnetic field around a current carrying conductor

Electromagnetism

When a current flows through a conductor, a magnetic field is produced around it (Fig. 7.1). The direction of the magnetic field is determined by the direction of the current.

The notation for the direction of current through a conductor is as shown in Fig. 7.2. The point in (a) can be thought of as the pointed end of an arrow or dart, while the cross in (b) can be thought of as the tail end view of the arrow or dart.

The magnetic field surrounding a conductor carrying a current is as shown in Fig. 7.3. The direction of the field can easily be remembered by thinking of a right-handed screw action. For Fig. 7.3(a), to screw inwards *in the direction* of the current, the screw should be turned in the clockwise direction, the direction of the magnetic field. For Fig. 7.3(b), imagine unscrewing the screw — the movement is in the anticlockwise direction.

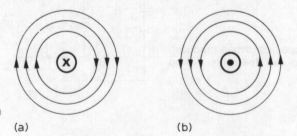

(a)   (b)

Field produced by two parallel conductors

(i)   Currents in the same direction

Figure 7.4(a) shows two conductors placed near each other with the magnetic field of each conductor drawn separately. The two fields oppose each other and cancel out between the conductors. The resultant is a single field surrounding both conductors as shown in (b). If the direction of the currents is reversed, the direction of the magnetic field will also be reversed as shown in (c).

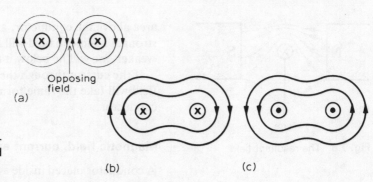

Fig. 7.4 (a) Two conductors with current going in the same direction (b) and (c) show resultant field

Fig. 7.5 (a) Two conductors with current going in opposite directions (b) The resultant field

(ii) Currents in opposite directions

Figure 7.5(a) shows the magnetic field of each conductor separately. This time the two fields are aiding each other in the middle. The resultant field is as shown in (b) with the magnetic field strongest between the conductors.

Field produced by a solenoid

A solenoid is a coil of wire as shown in Fig. 7.6. When current passes through it, the solenoid behaves like a magnetic bar with north and south poles. Its magnetic field is the same as that for a permanent magnet. The magnetic field can be strengthened by winding the solenoid coil round a magnetic core such as iron or steel. The current and the number of turns also determine the strength of the magnetic field.

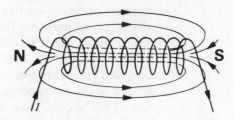

Fig. 7.6 Magnetic field around a solenoid

Electromagnet

One use of the solenoid is as an electromagnet. A soft magnetic material such as soft iron is used as the core. The solenoid behaves as a magnet only when there is current flowing through the coil. Electromagnets are used in electric bells and relays.

A conductor inside a magnetic field

Figure 7.7 shows a conductor carrying a current placed inside a magnetic field. It can be seen that the magnetic field of the conductor aids the magnetic field of the permanent magnet in the

Magnetic field due to conductor   Magnetic field due to poles

(a)

Fig. 7.7 Conductor inside a magnet field

(b)

Force

Fig. 7.8 The resultant field

area above the conductor, and opposes it in the area below it. A stronger magnetic field will thus lie above the conductor whilst a weaker one will lie below it (Fig. 7.8).

If the current through the conductor is reversed, the magnetic field will take the same form but with the strong field below the conductor.

Magnetic field, current and movement

A conductor placed inside a magnetic field will experience a force which tries to move it away from the strong magnetic field towards the weaker field as shown in Fig. 7.8. The direction of the force depends on the direction of current as well as the direction of the magnetic field. The magnitude of the force is determined by the strength of both the magnetic field and the current through the conductor.

The principle of producing movement of a conductor when placed in a magnetic field by passing a current through it is known as the **motor** principle and is used in electric motors, moving coil meters, and other devices.

If a conductor is moved across a magnetic field, a current is generated in the conductor. This is known as the **generator** principle and is used in dynamos and alternators.

Induced e.m.f.

So far, only the magnetic field due to direct current has been considered. The direction of the magnetic field is determined by the direction of the d.c. current. When an alternating current is used, an alternating magnetic field is set up. If a separate coil is now placed within this alternating field, an e.m.f. (voltage) will be induced in the coil. In other words, if two separate coils are placed near each other as shown in Fig. 7.9, then when an a.c. voltage is applied across one winding (W_1), a new a.c. voltage (the induced e.m.f.) will be observed across the terminals of the second winding (W_2). This is the principle of the transformer.

Input voltage V_1 a.c.

W_1 W_2

a.c. output voltage V_2

Fig. 7.9 Induced e.m.f.

The transformer

The transformer consists of two separate windings known as the *primary* and *secondary* windings. The input (a.c.) voltage is applied across the primary, producing a changing magnetic field. This changing magnetic field interacts with the secondary winding inducing an a.c. voltage across it. The induced voltage at the secondary has the same frequency as the input voltage but with its amplitude determined by the number of turns of both the primary and secondary windings.

If the input voltage at the primary   = V_1
the output voltage at the secondary   = V_2
the number of turns of the primary   = T_1
the number of turns of the secondary = T_2 then

$$\frac{V_1}{V_2} = \frac{T_1}{T_2}$$

Also, $\dfrac{I_1}{I_2} = \dfrac{T_2}{T_1}$ where I_1 and I_2 are primary and secondary currents.

Transformer efficiency

The above ratios assume that a transformer is 100% efficient, i.e. having no power loss. Hence

Input power $I_1 \times V_1$ = Output power $I_2 \times V_2$

In practice, transformers have efficiencies ranging from 96 to 99%.

To improve the efficiency of the transformer, both primary and secondary windings are wound on one magnetic core as shown in Fig. 7.10.

Fig. 7.10 The transformer

Step-up and step-down

A step-up transformer produces a higher voltage at the output (across its secondary) than the input voltage (across its primary). To achieve this the number of turns on the secondary has to be larger than those on the primary.

A step-down transformer produces a smaller voltage at its output because it has a smaller number of turns on its secondary than on its primary.

Fig. 7.11 Impedance ratio $r_1/r_2 = T_1^2/T_2^2 = n^2$

Impedance ratio

Consider the transformer shown in Fig. 7.11 with a load resistor r_2 connected across its secondary. Looking into the primary, an input resistance r_1 is observed which is the equivalent value of r_2 when transferred to the primary. The ratio r_1/r_2 is known as the resistance or impedance ratio of the transformer. This ratio may be derived as follows. Since $r_1 = V_1/I_1$ and $r_2 = V_2/I_2$, then

$$\frac{r_1}{r_2} = \frac{V_1}{I_1} \div \frac{V_2}{I_2} = \frac{V_1}{I_1} \times \frac{I_2}{V_2} = \frac{V_1}{V_2} \times \frac{I_2}{I_1}$$

But $V_1/V_2 = T_1/T_2 = n$ and $I_2/I_1 = T_1/T_2 = n$, therefore

$$\frac{r_1}{r_2} = n \times n = n^2$$

For example, if $r_2 = 100 \ \Omega$ and the turns ratio $T_1/T_2 = n = 2:1$, then looking into the primary winding, the transformer will be seen as a resistor $r_1 = 100 \ \Omega \times 2^2 = 100 \times 4 = 400 \ \Omega$.

Fig. 7.12 The auto-transformer

Auto-transformer

A transformer may be made with a single winding employing one tapping as shown in Fig. 7.12. T_1 is the number of turns of the primary and T_2 is the number of turns of the secondary. The voltage, current, impedance, and turns ratios have the same relationship as for an ordinary transformer.

Figure 7.13 shows another single winding transformer employing more than one tapping. The voltage, current, and impedance ratios are once again determined by the turns ratio, e.g. $v_1/v_a = T_1/T_a$ and $v_1/v_b = T_1/T_b$ and so on.

Fig. 7.13 An auto-transformer with multiple tappings

The centre tapped transformer

Figure 7.14 shows a transformer with a tap at the centre of its secondary. Two output voltages v_a and v_b are produced across each half of the secondary winding. The ratio of the input (primary) voltage to the secondary voltages is given by the turns ratio whereby

$$\frac{v_1}{v_a} = \frac{T_1}{T_a} \quad \text{and} \quad \frac{v_1}{v_b} = \frac{T_1}{T_b}$$

Fig. 7.14 The centre tapped transformer

where T_1, T_a and T_b are the number of turns of the primary, secondary a and secondary b respectively. Since the tapping is at the centre, v_a and v_b have equal amplitude. If the centre is earthed, as shown in Fig. 7.14, the two output waveforms are then in anti-phase to each other.

EXAMPLE

Refer to Fig. 7.15. (*a*) Calculate the voltage between transformer tappings B and C. (*b*) If there are 30 turns between tappings A and B, how many turns will the whole secondary winding have?

Solution

(*a*) Voltage between B and C = $v_{BC} = v_{AD} - v_{AB} - v_{CD}$
$$= 36\text{ V} - 6\text{ V} - 12\text{ V} = 18\text{ V}.$$

(*b*) $\dfrac{v_{AB}}{v_{AD}} = \dfrac{\text{Number of turns between A and B}}{\text{Number of turns between A and D}}$

Hence $\dfrac{6\text{ V}}{36\text{ V}} = \dfrac{30}{T_{AD}}$ or $T_{AD} = 30 \times \dfrac{36}{6} = 180\text{ turns}$

Fig. 7.15 $v_{AD} = 36$ V, $v_{AB} = 6$ V, $v_{CD} = 12$ V

The magnetic circuit

It is accepted that, in a magnetic circuit, the magnetic flux (or magnetic field) measured in Teslas is created by a force known as the magnetomotive force (m.m.f.). A magnetic circuit is usually compared with an electric circuit, where the flux corresponds to the current and the magnetomotive force m.m.f. corresponds to the electromotive force e.m.f. Just as an electric circuit is said to have a resistance, so a magnetic circuit is said to have a **reluctance** S which corresponds to resistance R. For example, a magnetic material such as soft iron has a low reluctance, i.e. low resistance to magnetic flux.

Permeability

The permeability of a material is a measure of the ease with which it may be magnetised. For example, soft iron and other electro-magnetic materials such as ferrites have high permeability. These materials are used in transformers, inductors, relays, and in ferrite aerials. On the other hand, non-magnetic materials have low permeability. Magnetic alloys such as silicon steel have the ability to retain their magnetism and are therefore used as permanent magnets in loudspeakers, moving-coil instruments, etc.

Screening

Consider the hollow cylinder, shown in Fig. 7.16, placed inside a magnetic field. If the cylinder is made of a low reluctance magnetic material, then the magnetic field will concentrate

Fig. 7.16 Magnetic screening

Fig. 7.17 Electrostatic screening as used in a transformer

through the cylinder as shown, with no magnetic flux passing through the space inside the cylinder. Consequently a body placed in this space would be screened or shielded from the magnetic field around it. Such screening, known as magnetic screening, is used to protect devices such as a cathode-ray tube, a moving-coil meter, or a loudspeaker from outside magnetic fields.

In transformers, another type of screening known as electro-static or electric screening is sometimes used. A screen or shield of thin copper sheet is placed between the primary and secondary windings as shown in Fig. 7.17. By earthing the screen, the effect of the capacitance that exists between the two windings due to their different potentials is minimized. Electrostatic screening is also used in coaxial cables and whenever conductors having different potentials are placed in close proximity.

8 Matching

Input and output impedance

Any device such as a simple amplifier or a complete TV receiver may be represented by a box with two input leads and two output leads (Fig. 8.1) and having an input impedance Z_{in} and an output impedance Z_o. Now, Z_{in} is the impedance of the device when looking into the input terminals AB, and Z_o is the impedance looking back into the output terminals CD. As far as the input signal is concerned, the device is a load impedance of Z_{in}. As far as the next stage of a load is concerned, the device looks like a generator with an internal impedance of Z_o.

In many cases, e.g. in power amplifiers or a receiving aerial feeding a radio or TV receiver, we wish to transfer power from one stage to the other. In these cases it is important that the maximum possible power is transferred. This is the purpose of impedance matching or maximum power transfer. Matching or maximum power transfer occurs when the output impedance of one stage is the same as the input impedance of the succeeding stage (Fig. 8.2).

Fig. 8.1 Input and output impedances Z_{in} and Z_o

Fig. 8.2 For matching $Z_o = Z_{in}$

Fig. 8.3

As an illustration, consider the circuit in Fig. 8.3 where a generator having an internal impedance of $r = 10 \, \Omega$ and an e.m.f. $e = 3$ V is used to feed a load resistance R. Maximum power transfer from the generator to the load takes place when load R = internal (or output) resistance of the generator.

For $R = 10 \, \Omega$, voltage across R, $V_R = 3/2 = 1.5$ V. Hence output power or power transferred into the load is

$$\frac{V^2}{R} = \frac{1.5 \times 1.5}{10} = \frac{2.25}{10} = 0.225 \text{ W} = 225 \text{ mW}.$$

Note that the power dissipated into the load is the same as that dissipated in the internal resistance r when the load is correctly matched.

For any other value of load R, the output power will be smaller than 225 mW. For $R = 20 \, \Omega$

$$V_R = \frac{3}{10 + 20} \times 20 = \frac{3 \times 20}{30} = 2 \text{ V}$$

giving an output power of $\dfrac{V^2}{R} = \dfrac{2 \times 2}{20} = \dfrac{4}{20} = 0.2$ W

$= 200$ mW.

Similarly if load R were reduced in value to say 10/2 or 5 Ω, then output power will be reduced to 200 mW.

Transformer matching

To ensure matching between two stages or between a load and an output stage in a circuit, a transformer is sometimes used as the *coupling device*. Figure 8.4 shows an a.f. power amplifier feeding into a loudspeaker load. Suppose that a 10 Ω loudspeaker is used with the amplifier having an output impedance of 1000 Ω. For matching to occur, the turns ratio $T_1/T_2 = n$ must be of such a value as to present 1000 Ω to the amplifier.

Output impedance
$r_1 = 1000\,\Omega$

$T_1 : T_2$

r_2
$10\,\Omega$

Fig. 8.4 Matching transformer. Turns ratio 10 : 1

But $n^2 = \dfrac{r_1}{r_2} = \dfrac{1000}{10} = 100$, hence $n = \sqrt{100} = 10$.

In other words, a step-down transformer must be used having a turns ratio of 10:1.

Note that in all cases where the amplifier is feeding a low impedance load (which is the majority of cases in practice), the matching transformer used must have a **step-down** turns ratio.

Examples

EXAMPLE 1

$15\,\Omega$
Amp.

R
$7\,\Omega$

$8\,\Omega$

Fig. 8.5

Figure 8.5 shows an amplifier feeding an 8 Ω loudspeaker in series with a 7 Ω resistor.

(a) State the purpose of R.
(b) What is the main disadvantage of using this method?

Solution

(a) The purpose of R is to ensure that the amplifier produces maximum power output.
(b) The disadvantage is that almost half of the output power is lost in the resistor.

EXAMPLE 2

C

$30\,\Omega$

R

Earphone socket

Fig. 8.6

Figure 8.6 shows a method used to provide a facility for earphone connection. State the value of R if the earphone has an impedance of 8 Ω.

Solution

$R = 30 - 8 = 22\ \Omega$.

Fig. 8.7

EXAMPLE 3

Refer to Fig. 8.7. How should two 15 Ω speakers be connected to the output transformer shown?

Solution

For matching to take place, output impedance presented by the transformer must be equal to the load resistance. This can be done by connecting the two speakers in parallel, thus giving a total load of 7.5 Ω across the common connection and the transformer tapping labelled 7.5 Ω.

EXAMPLE 4

Figure 8.8 shows a signal splitter network where an extra load is matched to the same source. Calculate the value of R.

Fig. 8.8

Solution

For matching the total resistance R_{AE} looking into AE must be 75 Ω. The total resistance R_{BE} between B and E (across the two load branches) is

$$\frac{1}{2}(R + 75) = \frac{R}{2} + \frac{75}{2}$$

Total resistance across AE is

$$R_{AE} = R + R_{BE} = R + \frac{R}{2} + \frac{75}{2} = \frac{3R}{2} + \frac{75}{2}$$

But for matching, $R_{AE} = 75$ Ω. Therefore

$$75 = \frac{3R}{2} + \frac{75}{2}$$

i.e. $\dfrac{3R}{2} = 75 - \dfrac{75}{2} = \dfrac{75}{2}$

$$R = \frac{75}{3} = 25 \ \Omega$$

9 Wave shaping

Fig. 9.1 Clipping

Clipping

The process of flattening one or both peaks of an a.c. waveform is known as clipping or limiting. It is achieved as we saw in the last section by overloading an amplifier. A large degree of clipping as seen in Fig. 9.1(c) can produce an approximate square wave from a sine wave input.

Clamping

A clamper is also known as a d.c. restorer. It provides an a.c. signal with a d.c. level which it did not have before. For example, clampers are used in tv receivers to give the video signal a d.c. level (Fig. 9.2).

Fig. 9.2 Clamping

A.C. coupling

The reverse of the d.c. restorer is the a.c. coupler which removes the d.c. level from the input (Fig. 9.3). The a.c. coupler is usually as simple as a single capacitor blocking the d.c. while allowing the a.c. to go through.

Fig. 9.3 a.c. coupling

Rectification

This is the process of transforming alternating current into direct current by allowing the current to flow in one direction only.

Rectifiers are used in d.c. power supplies and for various other purposes such as demodulators.

Rectification is achieved in one of two ways.

(*a*) Half wave rectification which cuts out either the negative or the positive half of the signal. Only one half of the cycle is produced at the output as shown in Fig. 9.4. Such waveforms have a d.c. level equal to 0.318 (approximately $\frac{1}{3}$) of the peak value.

(*b*) Full wave rectification which reproduces the two halves of the cycle, but now both in the same direction (Fig. 9.5). The d.c. level is now doubled to 0.636 (approximately two-thirds) of the peak value.

Fig. 9.4 Half wave rectification (b) shows d.c. level 0.318 V_p

Fig. 9.5 Full wave rectification (b) shows d.c. level = 0.636 V_p

Half wave rectification produces a signal having a frequency equal to the original wave while full wave rectification doubles the frequency of the original wave.

Filters

In electronics it is often necessary to separate one frequency band from another. A filter allows one frequency band through and cuts off all others. There are three main types of filter.

(a) The **high pass filter** allows only high frequencies to pass through with little loss and attenuates all low frequencies. For a complex wave input containing a number of harmonics, only the high frequency harmonics will pass through while the fundamental and lower harmonics will be greatly attenuated.

(b) The **low pass filter** allows low frequencies to pass through and attenuates all high frequencies. For a complex wave input only the fundamental and low harmonics will appear at the output of this type of filter, while higher harmonics will be greatly attenuated.

(c) The **band pass filter** allows only a specific range or band of frequencies through and cuts off all other frequencies above and below that band.

Square waves

As explained in Chapter 3, square waves are complex waveforms consisting of a fundamental and an infinite number of odd harmonics. The square wave thus consists of low-frequency components (the fundamental and the low harmonics) and high-frequency components (the high harmonics). On the square wave itself, the low-frequency components are represented by the flat top and the flat bottom, while the high-frequency components are represented by the fast rising or falling edges.

When a square wave is fed into a filter, one of its two components will be cut off, depending on the type of filter used.

The differentiator

The differentiator is a high pass filter, which when fed with a square wave reproduces the high-frequency components only, namely the fast rising and falling edges in the form of positive- and negative-going spikes. The output waveform is the short duration pulses or spikes shown in Fig. 9.6. Each cycle of the input wave produces two spikes at the output, of an amplitude equal to that of the input.

Fig. 9.6 Differentiation

The integrator

The integrator is a low pass filter which when fed with a square wave reproduces the low-frequency components only, namely the flat parts of the waveform. Ideally, only d.c. appears at the output. In practice, however, the output is a triangular wave with an amplitude smaller than that of the square-wave input (Fig. 9.7).

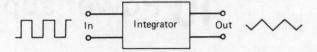

Fig. 9.7 Integration

The effect on a rectangular wave

Figure 9.8 shows the effect of differentiating and integrating a rectangular waveform.

RECTANGULAR
INPUT

DIFFERENTIATOR
OUTPUT

Fig. 9.8 Differentiating and integrating
a rectangular wave

INTEGRATOR
OUTPUT

The effect on a sine wave

A sine wave being a pure waveform will suffer no change in its shape when fed into any kind of filter such as a differentiator or an integrator. Only its amplitude will be affected. A differentiator being a high pass filter will, however, leave the amplitude of a high frequency sine wave unaffected. But a low frequency sine wave will suffer a reduction on its amplitude through a differentiator. The opposite is true for an integrator.

10 Power supplies I

Networks can be divided into two types, active networks and passive networks. Amplifiers and oscillators are active networks while resistors, attenuators and transformers are passive networks. Unlike passive networks which function merely by being connected in the circuit, active networks require d.c. power. This d.c. power can be provided by a battery or from a mains source.

The d.c. power supply is a circuit that transforms a.c. power into d.c. power. It is usually used to convert the mains into d.c. voltages of various magnitudes.

Block diagram

Figure 10.1 shows a block diagram for a d.c. power supply (*a*) using a half wave and (*b*) using a full wave rectifier. The a.c. input is usually taken from the mains. The first stage is the rectifier (either half wave or full wave rectifier). The output of the rectifier has a d.c. level together with a large a.c. variation. This

Fig. 10.1   d.c. power supply   (b)

waveform is known as a pulsating d.c. voltage which cannot be used as a satisfactory d.c. supply. In order to remove the a.c. content a smoothing circuit is used — which is a low pass filter allowing the d.c. to pass on and reducing the a.c. to a small ripple that appears at the output as shown. The frequency of the ripple is determined by the rectifier used. A half wave rectifier will produce a ripple frequency the same as the input, while full wave rectifiers double the frequency.

In many d.c. supplies, a transformer is used before the rectifier to change the a.c. input to the required voltage level (Fig. 10.2). The turns ratio of the transformer determines the d.c. output level produced.

Fig. 10.2 d.c. power supply using a transformer

Regulation curve

All d.c. supplies including batteries provide a maximum voltage under no-load condition, i.e. when the supply is providing no current. Due to internal resistance, the terminal voltage begins to fall below this maximum as load current is drawn from the supply. The way the terminal voltage changes with load current is known as the regulation of the power supply. A typical regulation curve is shown in Fig. 10.3.

Fig. 10.3 Regulation curve

Fig. 10.4 Regulated power supply

In order to improve the regulation of a d.c. supply, i.e. to keep the terminal voltage constant as load current is increased, regulators are used at the output. Figure 10.4 shows a block diagram for a regulated power supply.

11 Communication

The following four sections deal with the various methods of communication, in other words systems of information transmission. Transmission of information between persons can take many forms. Direct speech is one method – using sound waves through the air. Flag, lamp, or smoke signals are visual methods of communication that normally have a longer range than sound waves. In all these cases, information is conveyed only when a change occurs in the transmitted quantity. A continuous light from a bulb for instance conveys no information. It is only when the light is interrupted according to a certain code that information is passed on.

These systems of communication are limited in the distance they can cover and are dependent on atmospheric conditions. Sound waves can travel a few hundred metres but will be affected by the direction and speed of the wind. Lamp signals depend on clear weather, and so on.

Electrical communication

The use of electricity as a means of communication overcomes many of these difficulties. Electrical communication uses electric waves of one kind or another to transmit the information from one point to another by the use of a wire or without the use of a wire, i.e. wireless transmission.

Transducers

In any electrical communication system, the information to be transmitted such as speech, music or computer data must first be transformed into a changing current or voltage. At the receiving end, the electric wave of current or voltage must be converted back into the original information, i.e. speech, music or coded data. For instance, a microphone is used to transform sound waves into electrical waves, while at the receiving end a loudspeaker is used to convert the electrical waves back into sound waves. Such devices as microphones and loudspeakers are known as transducers.

As with the non-electrical systems of communication mentioned above, a stream of information cannot be transmitted by steady current (or voltage) or by a continuous tone of constant amplitude and frequency. Information can only flow between two points if a steady current or tone is varied in one way or another. The way this is achieved varies with the different methods of electrical communication.

Bandwidth of transmission

Fig. 11.1 Simple transmission system

The simplest system of electrical transmission is shown in Fig. 11.1. It consists of a battery and a key or switch at the sending end. At the receiving end an electrical bulb is used which is connected to the transmitting end by a wire called the transmission line. The simplest code for this system is as follows:

Switch ON (light on) means YES.
Switch OFF (light off) means NO.

If this information is to be transmitted once every one second, the bulb will go ON and OFF once every second. The waveform transmitted along the line is as shown in Fig. 11.2(a). The frequency of transmission is therefore 1 Hz.

If the information is now increased to 10 (ON and OFF or YES and NO) every second, the waveform will be as shown in Fig. 11.2(b) with 10 complete cycles in a period of 1 second. The frequency is therefore 10 Hz.

If on the other hand the information is to be varied between 1 and 10 (YES and NO) a second, the frequency of transmission will vary between 1 Hz and 10 Hz. In order to accommodate this type of transmission, the system must have a frequency range extending from 1 Hz to 10 Hz. This is known as the bandwidth of the system.

The bandwidth thus depends on the quantity and speed of information. Wider bandwidths are needed for greater amounts of information. Conversely, a system with a given bandwidth can only handle an amount of information determined by the band-

Fig. 11.2

width itself. In our previous example, if the bandwidth was limited to 10 Hz, the amount of information that can be transmitted will thus be limited to 10 YESES and NOES.

In practice the bandwidth is made as narrow as possible without damaging the information, in order to reduce costs. For example, a channel having a bandwidth of 300 Hz will occupy as much frequency space in a system as 3 channels each having a bandwidth of 100 Hz. The system with the narrower bandwidths is therefore more economical.

Telephony

The telephone system uses the principle of breaking a steady voltage by an a.f. signal. Figure 11.3 shows a simple block diagram for a telephone system.

Fig. 11.3 Telephony

Sound waves are transformed into electric waves by the microphone. The telephone line is kept at a d.c. potential of 50 V. This d.c. potential is broken by the a.c. waveform produced by the microphone as shown. An amplifier known as a repeater is used to make good any loss sustained by the signal due to the resistance of the line. More than one repeater may be used depending on the length of the line. At the receiving end, sound waves are reproduced by the speaker.

The telephone system has a bandwidth of 300 Hz to 3400 Hz or 3.1 kHz. This is a small portion of the complete a.f. range of 20 Hz–20 kHz, which is one reason for the poor quality of sound produced by telephones – but it is quite adequate for the purpose of speech.

Telegraphy

Figure 11.4 shows a simplified block diagram for a telegraph system. As the key at the transmitter is closed and opened, a train of pulses is transmitted along the line operating the relay at the

Fig. 11.4 Telegraphy

receiving end. The relay can be used to operate a switch or a bulb. The waveform of transmission is a sequence of pulses with varying Mark and Space.

Transmission is carried out according to a code (e.g. Morse Code) which allocates a particular Mark and Space time sequence for each letter of the alphabet.

Telegraphy is a relatively slow and cheap system of communication − the bandwidth is a mere 120 Hz, and 25 telegraph channels can be accommodated in one telephone channel:

$$\frac{\text{Telephone bandwidth}}{\text{Telegraph bandwidth}} = \frac{3100}{120} = 25.$$

A system of filters is required to separate one channel from the other.

Modulation

Information can be transmitted from point A to point B by varying an a.c. waveform. The information referred to as the signal is used to change some property of a high frequency wave in such a way as to contain the signal within it. This process is known as modulation.

The high frequency wave is called the **carrier** and after modulation is referred to as the *modulated carrier*.

With modulation, the signal or information is no longer transmitted directly, rather it is 'carried' by the carrier.

Demodulation

At the receiving end, the information has to be extracted from the modulated carrier to reproduce the original signal. This is known as demodulation or detection.

Types of modulation

There are many types of modulation depending on what property of the high frequency carrier is changed by the signal. If the amplitude of the carrier is changed according to the signal, it is known as amplitude modulation. If the frequency of the carrier is changed, it is known as frequency modulation, and so on. The various types of modulation will be dealt with later.

Radio transmission

Radio transmission is wireless transmission using electromagnetic waves, which travel through space at 3×10^8 m/s, the velocity of light.

Visible light occupies a small band of the electromagnetic frequency scale (or spectrum) to which the eye is sensitive. Just as the ear is sensitive to a band of sound waves, so the eye is sensitive to a band of electromagnetic waves called light waves. The various sensations of colour are produced by the different frequencies within the light wave band.

Figure 11.5 shows the frequency scale for electromagnetic waves. Up to frequencies of 300 000 MHz, the electromagnetic waves are known as radio waves, which are used as carriers for radio transmission. Radio or wireless transmission uses an aerial to radiate the modulated radio waves and another to receive them.

Radio waves are divided into a number of bands as shown in the Table and Fig. 11.5.

VLF (very low frequency)		below 30 kHz
LF (low frequency)	LW (long wave)	30–300 kHz
MF (medium frequency)	MW (medium wave)	300–3000 kHz
HF (high frequency)	SW (short wave)	3000–30 000 kHz
VHF (very high frequency)		30–300 MHz
UHF (ultra high frequency)		300–3000 MHz
SHF (super high frequency)		3000–30 000 MHz
EHF (extra high frequency)		30 000–300 000 MHz

Fig.   11.5 Electromagnetic   waves, frequency scale

12 Amplitude modulation

Amplitude modulation (a.m.) is the most commonly used type of modulation. In the a.m. system, the amplitude of the carrier is varied in accordance with the signal or information (Fig. 12.1). With no signal, the carrier has a constant level as in Fig. 12.1(b). When modulated by a sine wave signal, the amplitude of the carrier changes above and below its unmodulated level as the signal goes up and down. The larger the signal the greater is the change in the amplitude of the carrier. The amplitude modulated carrier (Fig. 12.1(c)) has an envelope which is a replica of the modulating signal. When demodulating an a.m. carrier, it is this envelope that is extracted to reproduce the signal.

Fig. 12.1 Amplitude modulation (50% modulation depth)

Modulation depth

The ratio of the signal peak to the carrier peak is known as the modulation depth. It tells us the amount by which the level of carrier is changing due to the signal. Modulation depth is always given as a percentage and for this reason it is also referred to as percentage modulation.

$$\text{Modulation depth} = \frac{\text{Signal peak}}{\text{Carrier peak}} \times 100\% \text{ (see Fig. 12.1)}$$

For instance if the signal peak is 1 V and the carrier peak is

2 V, then modulation depth $= \dfrac{1V}{2V} \times 100\% = 50\%$.

The a.m. carrier shown in Fig. 12.1 has a modulation depth of 50%.

Over-modulation

Figure 12.2(a) shows an a.m. carrier with 100% modulation. Modulation depths above 100% produce distortion (Fig. 12.2(b)). For this reason modulation depth is limited to a maximum value which for BBC transmission is 80%.

Side frequencies

The amplitude-modulated carrier waveform can be shown to contain three pure sine wave components each of constant amplitude but of a different frequency. The three components are the carrier itself together with the two side frequencies f_1 and f_2. Each signal frequency produces two separate side frequencies. If the signal frequency is f_s and the carrier frequency is f_c, then

$f_1 = f_c - f_s$ known as the lower side frequency

$f_2 = f_c + f_s$ known as the upper side frequency.

For example, if the frequency of the carrier is 100 kHz and that of the signal is 1 kHz, then

the upper side frequency $f_2 = 100 + 1 = 101$ kHz

the lower side frequency $f_1 = 100 - 1 = 99$ kHz.

The a.m. waveform, i.e. the carrier and its two side frequencies, can be represented on what is known as a frequency spectrum by three arrows, each representing a pure sine wave (Fig. 12.3).

(a)

Distortion

(b)

Fig. 12.2 (a) 100% modulation (b) Over-modulation

Fig. 12.3 Frequency spectrum for a.m. carrier

Fig. 12.4 Sidebands

Fig. 12.5 Sidebands and bandwidth for carrier modulated by a single sine wave

Fig. 12.6

Sidebands

Information signals are nearly always of complex form containing a number of pure sine waves. Since each pure sine wave produces a pair of side frequencies, a complex wave will produce numerous side frequencies and thus creating a band of frequencies on either side of the carrier (Fig. 12.4). These are known as the sidebands. The range between the highest and lowest upper side frequencies f_2 and f_4 is known as the upper sideband (USB). Similarly, the range between the highest and lowest lower side frequencies f_3 and f_1 is known as the lower sideband (LSB).

The two sidebands are symmetrical about the carrier and each contain the same information as the other. The carrier contains no information. All the information is in fact carried by the side frequencies.

For a single sine wave signal, the upper and lower sidebands are assumed to extend from the carrier to the upper and lower side frequencies (Fig. 12.5).

EXAMPLE 1

A 100 kHz carrier is amplitude modulated by a signal having a frequency range of 400–3400 Hz. State the sidebands produced.

Solution

The highest signal frequency, 3400 Hz, produces two side frequencies:

$$f_1 = 100\ 000 - 3400 = 96\ 600\ \text{Hz} \quad \text{and}$$
$$f_2 = 100\ 000 + 3400 = 103\ 400\ \text{Hz}$$

(Fig. 12.6).
The lowest signal frequency, 400 Hz, produces a further two side frequencies:

$$f_3 = 100\ 000 - 400 = 99\ 600\ \text{Hz} \quad \text{and}$$
$$f_4 = 100\ 000 + 400 = 100\ 400\ \text{Hz}.$$

The upper sideband USB $= f_2 - f_4 = 103\ 400 - 100\ 400$
$$= 3000\ \text{Hz}$$
The lower sideband LSB $= f_3 - f_1 = \ \ 99\ 600 - 96\ 600$
$$= 3000\ \text{Hz}$$

In other words,

$$\text{USB} = \text{LSB} = \text{highest signal frequency} - \text{lowest signal frequency}$$
$$= 3400 - 400 = 3000\ \text{Hz}$$

The side frequencies of any other signal frequency will fall within the upper and lower sidebands.

Bandwidth

Since the side frequencies carry the information, for faithful transmission the bandwidth of the system must be large enough to accommodate all side frequencies present. For a pure sine wave signal, two side frequencies are produced. The bandwidth thus extends from the lower side frequency f_1 in Fig. 12.5 to the upper side frequency f_2.

If the signal frequency is 1 kHz, then

$$USB = LSB = 1 \text{ kHz and}$$
$$\begin{aligned} \text{Bandwidth} &= LSB + USB \\ &= 2 \times \text{sideband} \\ &= 2 \times 1 \text{ kHz} = 2 \text{ kHz} \end{aligned}$$

In other words, bandwidth = 2 × signal frequency.

For a complex signal, the bandwidth of the a.m. system = 2 × highest signal frequency, and in this way all side frequencies are included.

Single and double sideband transmission

Since one sideband contains as much information as the other, transmission *can* be carried out using one sideband only without any loss of information. In single sideband transmission (SSB), either the lower or the upper sideband is suppressed at the sending end and the only remaining sideband is transmitted. In double sideband transmission (DSB), both sidebands are transmitted.

Single sideband transmission requires half the bandwidth needed for double sideband transmission. For this reason SSB transmission is used in telephony and radio. Twice as many channels can thus be fitted within one band of carrier frequencies. For simplicity DSB transmission is used for all a.m. sound broadcast radio. Normally, DSB transmission is assumed unless otherwise stated.

EXAMPLE

An a.m. carrier is modulated by a square wave of frequency 100 Hz. Neglecting harmonics above the fifth, state the bandwidth required for (a) DSB and (b) SSB transmission.

Solution

A 100 Hz square wave contains the following:

the fundamental = 100 Hz
the 3rd harmonic = 3 × 100 = 300 Hz
the 5th harmonic = 5 × 100 = 500 Hz

Higher harmonics are neglected.
Thus the highest signal frequency = 500 Hz
Bandwidth for DSB = 2 × highest signal frequency
    = 2 × 500 = 1000 Hz
Bandwidth for SSB transmission = $\frac{1}{2}$ DSB = $\frac{1}{2}$ × 1000
    = 500 Hz.

The amplitude modulated radio transmitter

In the radio transmitter, the sound waves are first transformed into electric waves (the a.f. modulating signal) by the microphone (Fig. 12.7). The a.f. signal is amplified by an a.f. amplifier (stage 1) to be fed into the a.m. modulator (stage 2). The carrier wave is generated by an r.f. oscillator (stage 5), amplified by an r.f. amplifier (stage 6) tuned to the particular carrier frequency, and fed into the a.m. modulator. The a.m. carrier is then amplified by stage 3 and fed into the r.f. power output amplifier. The output stage drives the r.f. (i.e. carrier) power into the aerial. The bandwidth of the a.m. radio transmission is restricted to 9 kHz using double sideband transmission.

Fig. 12.7 Block diagram of an a.m. transmitter

The amplitude modulated radio receiver

A radio receiver is required to operate over a range of carrier frequencies (e.g. the MW and LW bands) and must produce an a.f. output which is a faithful reproduction of the original modulating signal. The receiver must be capable of selecting the desired carrier frequency (i.e. the desired station) to the exclusion of all others.

The tuned radio frequency receiver (TRF)

Figure 12.8 shows a block diagram for a TRF radio receiver. Stages 1 and 2 are two similar amplifiers ganged together. This way both amplifiers are always tuned to the same carrier frequency. By tuning the r.f. amplifiers, the desired carrier frequency is selected and amplified. The selected a.m. carrier is then demodulated by the detector reproducing the a.f. signal. This is followed by an a.f. voltage amplifier (stage 4) and an a.f. output power stage which drives a.f. power into the loudspeaker load.

The TRF set, also known as the straight set, is no longer made

Fig. 12.8 TRF radio receiver

commercially as it suffers from a number of disadvantages. The main disadvantage is that every r.f. stage (stages 1 and 2) has to be tunable to the whole frequency band, e.g. for the MW band from 600–1600 kHz. The tuning of both r.f. stages has to occur simultaneously, hence the ganging. This creates a number of difficulties in mechanical design as well as in the selectivity of the amplifiers.

The superhet receiver

In order to overcome the disadvantages of the TRF set, the superheterodyne principle was introduced. The carrier frequency selected by the tuner is changed, using a frequency changer, to a common frequency referred to as the **intermediate frequency, the i.f.** The tuned r.f. amplifiers can thus be tuned to one frequency only, namely the intermediate frequency. For a.m. radio sets, an i.f. of 470 kHz is commonly used.

Frequency changing

Frequency changing is achieved by a mixer and a local oscillator (Fig. 12.9). Two separate r.f. signals are fed into the mixer, the received carrier frequency f_c and the local oscillator frequency f_o.

Fig. 12.9 Frequency changing

The mixer produces four different frequencies: the two original ones, f_c and f_o, together with their sum, $f_o + f_c$, and their difference, $f_o - f_c$. The output is tuned to the difference $f_o - f_c$ and this is the intermediate frequency. The frequency of the local oscillator is made greater than the carrier frequency by the i.f. 470 kHz at all times. This is achieved by ganging the local oscillator to the r.f. tuner.

Block diagram of a superhet receiver

The carrier frequency is selected by the r.f. tuner and subsequently changed to the intermediate frequency by the mixer (Fig. 12.10). Stages 4 and 5 are r.f. amplifiers (known as i.f. amplifiers) tuned to the i.f., 470 kHz. The modulated i.f. is fed into the a.m. detector which extracts the a.f. information feeding it into the a.f. section and so to the loudspeakers.

Fig. 12.10 The superhet radio receiver

Bandwidths

The bandwidth of the a.m. radio system is restricted to 9 kHz. To avoid overlap between adjacent transmissions, it follows that each sideband should be only 4.5 kHz, giving a highest signal frequency of 4.5 kHz. The bandwidth of the r.f. tuning stage and the i.f. amplifiers must therefore be 9 kHz to accommodate both sidebands, while that for the a.f. amplifiers need not be higher than 4.5 kHz to accommodate the highest signal frequency.

13 Frequency modulation

The other common type of modulation used in radio communication is frequency modulation (f.m.) where the frequency of the carrier changes in accordance with the modulating signal (Fig. 13.1).

Signal

Carrier

Frequency modulated carrier

Fig. 13.1 Frequency modulation. Note the amplitude of the carrier remaining constant as its frequency changes

Frequency deviation

Frequency deviation is the amount by which the carrier frequency changes for a change of 1 V in the signal level. The unit for frequency deviation is kHz/V. For example, suppose a carrier of frequency 1000 kHz is to be frequency modulated by a square wave having an amplitude of 5 V (Fig. 13.2). If the frequency deviation is given as 10 kHz/V, then for the period from A to B, the carrier frequency will be increased by

$$\text{Signal amplitude} \times \text{Frequency deviation} = 5 \times 10$$
$$= 50 \text{ kHz}$$

Fig. 13.2 F.M. carrier modulated by a square wave

giving a carrier frequency of 1000 kHz + 50 kHz

$$= 1050 \text{ kHz}.$$

From B to C the carrier frequency will deviate by a similar amount, namely 5 × 10 = 50 kHz, but this time in the negative direction giving a smaller carrier frequency of 1000 − 50 = 950 kHz.

Maximum deviation

The change in the carrier frequency due to the signal level has to be limited to a maximum value which the carrier is not allowed to exceed. This is known as the maximum deviation. For example, BBC f.m. transmission uses a frequency deviation of 15 kHz/V and a maximum deviation of ± 75 kHz. The maximum signal is limited by the maximum permissible deviation.

$$\text{Maximum signal} = \frac{\text{Maximum deviation}}{\text{Frequency deviation}} = \frac{\pm 75}{15} = \pm 5 \text{ V}$$

or in other words, 5 V in the positive direction or the negative direction.

Side frequencies and bandwidth

When a carrier is frequency modulated with one signal frequency, a large number of side frequencies are produced. The amplitude of the side frequencies gets progressively smaller as they get further away from the carrier.

The bandwidth of an f.m. system has then to be of infinite width to accommodate all the side frequencies. In practice, the smaller side frequencies can be neglected without any noticeable distortion. The BBC for instance uses a bandwidth of 250 kHz for its f.m. transmission.

Comparison between a.m. and f.m. systems

		Amplitude modulation	*Frequency modulation*
1.	Carrier amplitude	Changes with the signal	Remains constant
2.	Side frequencies	Two for each signal frequency	Indefinite number
3.	Bandwidth	9 kHz	250 kHz
4.	Waveband	LW, MW, SW	VHF, UHF

Advantages of frequency modulation

f.m. is superior to a.m. transmission in the following ways:

1. A better quality sound is possible with the f.m. system. This is because of the large bandwidth which can accommodate a greater number of harmonics.
2. F.m. transmission has very low noise level. Noise is unwanted signals that appear at the output, usually in the form of a change in the amplitude of the carrier. In the f.m. system, this can easily be removed by clipping both peaks of the carrier wave. The information contained in the changing frequency of the carrier remains unaltered.

The frequency modulated transmitter

The f.m. transmitter (Fig. 13.3) is similar to the a.m. transmitter except for the modulation (stage 3). Frequency modulation is achieved by an r.f. oscillator whose frequency is varied according to the a.f. signal fed into it from the a.f. amplifier (stage 2).

BBC f.m. transmission data

Type	double sideband
Bandwidth	250 kHz
Frequency deviation	15 kHz/V
Maximum deviation	±75 kHz
Carrier	VHF: 89.1, 91.5, 93.5 MHz

Fig. 13.3 F.M. transmitter

The frequency modulated receiver

Figure 13.4 shows a block diagram for a superhet f.m. receiver.

Fig. 13.4 F.M. receiver

The first stage of the f.m. receiver is a tuned r.f. amplifier replacing the tuner in the a.m. receiver. This stage is necessary in f.m. receivers to provide enough amplification of the VHF carrier. The local oscillator together with the mixer (stages 2 and 3) change the selected carrier frequency to an intermediate frequency of 10.7 MHz. This is followed by the i.f. amplifiers. The f.m. detector or decoder (often a radio detector) translates the frequency deviations into the original a.f. signal which is fed into the a.f. section and so to the loudspeaker load.

The bandwidth of the f.m. system is 250 kHz. This means that the r.f. and the i.f. amplifiers must have the same bandwidth, namely 250 kHz. The a.f. section (stages 7 and 8) has a bandwidth of 20 Hz–20 kHz approximately.

Automatic gain control (a.g.c.)

On many occasions, due to such things as atmospheric conditions, the received carrier level varies or 'fades', causing annoying variations in the output of the receiver. This can be overcome by the use of automatic gain control in both a.m. and f.m. receivers.

A.g.c. is achieved by the d.c. feedback network shown in Fig.

13.5. The d.c. output of the detector is fed back to the input of the first i.f. stage. The feedback voltage controls the gain of the i.f. amplifier in such a way as to increase the gain when the received carrier is weak and decrease it when the received carrier is strong.

Fig. 13.5 Automatic gain control (a.g.c.)

Automatic frequency control (a.f.c.)

A distorted output from a radio receiver can be caused by incorrect tuning. To obtain the correct tuning, automatic frequency control is used, mainly in f.m. receivers. A.f.c. controls the frequency of the local oscillator, using a discriminator (or comparator) shown in Fig. 13.6. The discriminator translates incorrect intermediate frequencies into a 'control voltage' which adjusts the frequency of the oscillator.

Fig. 13.6 Automatic frequency control (a.f.c.)

14 Pulse modulation

The types of modulation discussed so far have been those employing a continuous carrier. Another type of modulation is possible in which the carrier is discontinuous and exists as a train of pulses. Some characteristic of the pulse is then modified in accordance with the modulating signal.

1. **Pulse amplitude modulation** (PAM) where the amplitude of the pulse changes in accordance with the signal (Fig. 14.1(a)).
2. **Pulse width modulation** (PWM) where the width or duration of the pulse changes in accordance with the signal (Fig. 14.1(b)).
3. **Pulse position modulation** (PPM) where the position of the pulse changes in accordance with the signal (Fig. 14.1(c)).

Pulse code modulation (PCM)

In pulse amplitude modulation the modulating signal is used to vary the amplitude of a train of pulses. The pulse repetition frequency is constant and so also is the pulse width. Hence it follows that the amplitude variation of the pulses is the only quantity that is significant as far as transmitting the information is concerned.

Fig. 14.1 Pulse modulation

If instead of direct transmission of the pulses, the amplitude of each pulse is indicated by some code and this code is then transmitted, the resulting system is known as pulse code modulation (Fig. 14.2).

Fig. 14.2 Sampling and coding for PCM system

Voltage level	Pulse	Binary code
7	⎍⎍⎍⎍	111
6	⎍⎍⎍	110
5	⎍_⎍	101
4	⎍_	100
3	_⎍⎍	011
2	_⎍	010
1	_⎍	001
0	___	000

Fig. 14.3

In this system, the level of each pulse or sample is represented by a series of pulses of constant amplitude and frequency according to a binary code (see chapter 17). The arrangement of these, i.e. their occurrence or non-occurrence, represents the level of the pulse. For example a 3-digit binary code uses a series of three pulses to represent the level, as shown in Fig. 14.3.

By using a 3-digit binary only 7 discrete levels can be translated or coded into binary. A 4-digit binary could translate 15 levels and so on.

At the sending end, an encoding stage is employed to translate each level into a series of pulses. These series of pulses are then transmitted one after the other along the line. At the receiving end, a decoder is used to interpret the coded levels into the original information. A simplified block diagram for a PCM system is shown in Fig. 14.4.

PCM is relatively free from distortion and noise. Its other advantage is that it uses the same coding system as computer data

Fig. 14.4 PCM block diagrams

transmission, hence both can be carried out using the same encoding, decoding, amplifying and transmitting equipment.

Time division multiplexing

By using an interrupted carrier, i.e. a train of pulses, the modulating signal is sampled at regular intervals and its level is inspected and transmitted each time there is a pulse. In the interval between the samples, no information is sent. These intervals can thus be used to transmit samples of other signals. This way one channel can be used for a number of separate transmissions. This method is known as time division multiplexing.

15 The cathode ray oscilloscope

The cathode ray tube (CRT)

The principle of operation of the CRT is that a negatively charged hot cathode emits electrons which are attracted to and collected by a positively charged anode. This is the principle of the old thermionic valve.

In the CRT, high-speed electrons are emitted by an electron gun (Fig. 15.1). They are focussed by an electron lens and directed towards the screen which acts as the positively charged anode. The screen is coated on the inside with fluorescent powder (or phosphor) which gives a visible glow when struck by the high-speed electrons. The electron beam generated by the electron gun produces a stationary spot on the screen. In order to produce a trace, the electron beam has to be deflected in both the horizontal and vertical directions, X and Y.

Fig. 15.1 Block diagram for the cathode ray tube

Deflection methods

Two methods are used to deflect the beam in a CRT. The *electrostatic* method using two plates facing each other and an electric potential across them (Fig. 15.2a). An electrostatic field is thus created which deflects the electrons passing through it. *Electromagnetic* deflection on the other hand uses the magnetic field created by a current passing through a coil to deflect the elec-

(a)

(b)

Fig. 15.2 (a) Electrostatic deflection (b) Electromagnetic deflection

trons. Two sets of deflecting coils (known as scanning coils in a TV receiver) are used as shown in Fig. 15.2b. Both methods are capable of producing linear deflection. However, electrostatic deflection has a wider frequency range, hence its use in cathode ray oscilloscopes. Electromagnetic deflection is more suitable for high tube voltages such as used in a TV receiver and requires less space since both coils are placed at the same position along the neck of the tube.

Construction of the CRT

Figure 15.3 shows a schematic diagram of the internal construction of the cathode ray tube using electrostatic deflection. It also shows the various electrodes and their relative potentials. Electrons emitted from the cathode (or electron gun) pass through a small hole (or aperture) in the grid. The grid potential determines the intensity or number of electrons emitted and thus the brightness of the trace on the screen. The electron beam then passes through an electron lens which focusses the beam on the screen. A_3 is the final anode with a potential of a few kV (with respect to the cathode), referred to as the extra high tension or EHT. Two pairs of deflecting plates D_1 and D_2 are used to provide electrostatic deflection of the beam in the vertical and the horizontal directions respectively.

Fig. 15.3 The cathode ray tube

The vertical deflection is produced by the Y-plates, while the horizontal deflection is produced by the X-plates. The input signal is fed to the Y-plates which then deflect the electron beam up and down in accordance with the amplitude of the signal.

The X-plates cause the beam to travel from one side of the screen to the other (the sweep) at a steady pace and then return *very* quickly to its original position (flyback).

The input to the X-plates is a saw-tooth waveform shown in Fig. 15.4, generated by an oscillator. This waveform is known as the **time base**.

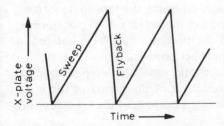

Fig. 15.4 Time base (saw-tooth) waveform

The appropriate application of signals to both the X and Y shift displaces the electron beam to produce a faithful trace of the input waveform on the screen.

The cathode ray oscilloscope (CRO)

The CRO employs a cathode ray tube together with the necessary devices to produce a stationary trace identical in form to the original input. Figure 15.5 shows a block diagram of the signal and time-base circuitry.

Fig. 15.5 CRO block diagram

Fig. 15.6

The height of the trace is determined by the Y-attenuator (or control) and the Y-amplifier giving a calibrated measurement of the amplitude of the input in volts/cm. The time-base oscillator is synchronised with the input to the Y-plates to produce a stationary trace on the screen.

Figure 15.6 shows the X and Y plates of a CRO fed with the signals shown. The signal connected across the Y plates causes the beam, and therefore the spot on the screen, to move up and down in the vertical direction. The saw-tooth waveform connected across the X plates causes the beam to move across the screen in the horizontal direction, with a constant speed during the sweep part of the waveform. At the end of the sweep the waveform drops quickly to its starting voltage, returning the spot to its starting point. During each sweep period the horizontal displacement is proportional to time, thus the timebase may be calibrated in terms of time, namely seconds per centimetre.

For synchronisation to occur, the timebase sweep is arranged to be equal to or a whole multiple of the period of the input signal, e.g. 2, 3, 4, etc. This is the purpose of the synchronising circuit.

Figure 15.7 shows a timebase having a sweep period which is

(a)

(b)

←—— 2 cycles ——→

Sweep

(c)

Fig. 15.7

twice that of the input signal. For every sweep, two cycles of the input are covered; hence the display will be as shown in Fig. 15.7(c). If the timebase frequency is now doubled, i.e. the sweep is halved, making it equal to the period of the input, the trace will be as shown in Fig. 15.8(a), displaying one cycle only. Conversely, if the timebase frequency is halved (i.e. doubling the sweep duration), the trace will cover twice as many cycles of the input in this case, displaying four cycles, as shown in Fig. 15.8(b).

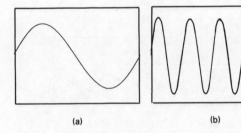

Fig. 15.8

(a)

(b)

Typical electrode potentials

CRT electrode potentials differ, depending on the size of the CRT screen. Further higher potentials are necessary in tubes used in television receivers than in those used in oscilloscopes.

Typical potentials are:

	Oscilloscope	Television
Cathode	− 30 V	− 70 V
Grid	0 V	0 V
Focussing lens	+ 1400 V	2−3 kV
Final anode	+ 2000 V	15−20 kV (mono)
		20−25 kV (colour)

EXAMPLE 1

The X and Y plates of an oscilloscope are fed with the following signals. For each case, sketch the expected display on the screen.

Solution

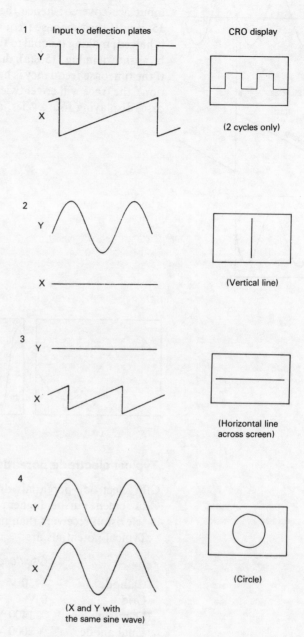

Fig. 15.9

16 Television

Television transmission involves transmitting picture as well as sound information. This necessitates a system with a wide bandwidth to accommodate the greater amount of information. For this reason carriers in the UHF band are used.

In the television system, the picture to be transmitted is produced by an electron camera on a specially formed light-sensitive plate which is then scanned by an electron beam. As the transmitted scene normally involves movement, it has to be scanned in a time short enough to make consecutive images only very slightly different from each other. The phenomenon of 'persistence of vision' in the eye then gives the viewer the impression of a moving picture just as a cine film does.

Scanning

The process of scanning involves exploring the picture in a series of lines, so that the degree of brightness is examined at each point in succession (Fig. 16.1). In the TV system, 25 complete pictures are scanned every second. In the British system the number of lines in each picture is 625.

Fig. 16.1 Scanning lines

Interlacing

Although 25 pictures per second produce the effect of continuous motion, such a picture suffers from severe flicker. This can be overcome by increasing the picture frequency to 50 pictures per second. As this would double the bandwidth required, the method of interlacing is used. First, all the odd lines are scanned, followed by the even ones. Each half picture is known as a 'field' or 'frame'. Hence there are 50 fields every second. The eye sees 50 half pictures every second which are nearly identical − the effect is virtually the same as seeing 50 pictures a second, and this removes the flicker.

The video waveform

The video waveform consists of the entire sequence of picture signals as scanned line by line. The start of each line and field is indicated by the use of synchronising pulses (sync pulses). Two different sync pulses are used: a line sync pulse at the beginning of each line (Fig. 16.2) and a field sync pulse at the beginning of each field. The field sync pulses occur 50 times every second giving a field frequency of 50 Hz. The line sync pulses have a much higher repetitive rate. Using the 625 British system, the line sync pulses occur 625 times for every complete picture giving 625×25 = 15 625 lines per second or a line frequency of 15 625 Hz (15.625 kHz).

Fig. 16.2 Video waveform

The sync pulses are all below the black level as can be seen in Fig. 16.2. The flyback thus takes place while the tube is blanked out, producing no trace on the screen.

The 625 system

This system uses 625 lines per picture.

Carrier	UHF band (400–900 MHz)
Modulation	video is a.m., sound is f.m.
Video bandwidth	5.5 MHz
Field frequency	50 Hz
Line frequency	15.625 kHz

Vestigial sideband transmission

The method of modulation in use for transmitting TV signals is amplitude modulation. Ordinary a.m. gives rise to two sets of sidebands on either side of the carrier. Since one sideband contains the same information as the other, the information contained in the modulated carrier can be conveyed by one sideband only, thus effectively halving the bandwidth. However, in practice it is impossible to achieve wideband modulation with one sideband completely eliminated. A gradual cut-off of one sideband is employed as shown in Fig. 16.3. The reduction of information by the gradual cut-off of the upper sideband between the carrier frequency f_c and f_2 is made up by transmitting a vestige (i.e. a part) of the lower sideband f_1 to f_c. This is known as vestigial sideband transmission.

Fig. 16.3 Vestigial sideband

The TV receiver

At the receiving end, a CRT is used to reproduce the picture. The beam is made to deflect in accordance with the original scanning of the picture at the studio. This is secured by the sync pulses present in the received waveform. Unlike the CRT used in oscilloscopes, electromagnetic deflection, using *coils*, is employed for TV receivers to reduce the length of the tube.

Block diagram (Fig. 16.4)

The radio wave signal is received by the aerial and the particular

Fig. 16.4 Complete block diagram for 625 TV receiver

Fig. 16.5 Simplified block diagram for 625 TV receiver

station is selected by the r.f. amplifier (stage 1) which also provides the first stage of amplification of the carrier. The mixer-oscillator (stage 2 and 3) changes the carrier frequency to an intermediate frequency of 39.5 MHz. The i.f. is amplified by the i.f. amplifier (stage 4) and fed into the a.m. detector (stage 5) for demodulation. The detected signal contains the video or picture information together with the sync pulses and the sound information. These three component parts have to be separated and fed into their individual channels.

At the output of the a.m. detector, the f.m. sound is separated and fed into the sound channel (see also Fig. 16.5). The remaining video and sync pulses are amplified by the video amplifier to be separated at its output. The picture information goes directly to the cathode of the CRT, while the sync pulses are fed into the time base channel.

The sound channel

The sound signal is in the form of a frequency modulated carrier at an intermediate frequency of 6 MHz. This is amplified (stage 12), detected by an f.m. detector (stage 13), and passed through the a.f. output stage (stage 14) to the loudspeaker.

The time base channel

The sync pulses are separated from the picture information at the output of the video amplifier (Figs. 16.4 and 16.5). They first go into a sync separator (stage 7) to separate the line and field sync pulses. Each sync pulse is then used to trigger its own oscillator (stages 8 and 10) to obtain the deflecting saw-tooth waveforms which are fed into their respective output stage. The line output also feeds the extra high tension (e.h.t.) stage which provides the 10−20 kV necessary for the final anode of the tube.

Colour television

As explained in Chapter 11, visible light occupies a band of frequencies within the electromagnetic spectrum. The sensation of colour is produced by the different frequencies within the visible spectrum (Fig. 16.6). The following colours can be observed, in *ascending* order of frequency:

Red   Orange   Yellow   Green   Blue   Indigo   Violet

As a useful aid to memory, the initial letters of the following sentence are in the same order as those for the spectrum colours:

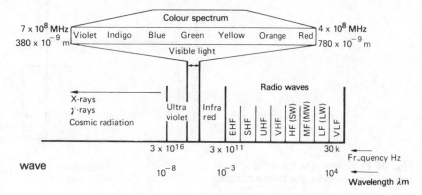

Fig. 16.6 Electromagnetic wave spectrum

Richard Of York Gave Battle In Vain

These are in the same order as the resistor colour code except that indigo is not used in this code. Red is 2, orange is 3, and so on.

Primary colours

Colours can be created by mixing other colours together. In colour TV, the various colours are produced by mixing *red, green* and *blue* (R, G, B) in different proportions. These three colours are known as primary colours. While an infinite variety of colours can be created by different mixtures of R, G and B, the following general rules should be committed to memory:

R + G = *yellow*
R + B = *magenta*
B + G = *cyan*
R + G + B = *white*

Colour transmission

One basic requirement of colour TV transmission is that a monochrome (black and white) TV set should be capable of receiving colour transmission and producing a normal black and white picture without any modification to the set. This is known as compatibility between colour and monochrome transmissions.

In order to meet this requirement, colour TV transmission is carried out by sending the monochrome (known as the luminance) information in the normal way. The colour content (known as the chrominance) is used to modulate a sub-carrier of 4.43 MHz added to the monochrome signal as shown in Fig. 16.7.

At the studio, three different cameras are used to explore the colour content of the picture. An appropriate filter is placed in

Fig. 16.7 Colour TV transmission. A sub-carrier is used for the colour content

front of each allowing only one primary colour through, e.g. a red filter for the 'red' camera and similarly for green and blue.

Fig. 16.8 Block diagram for a colour TV receiver

The TV colour receiver

Figure 16.8 shows a block diagram for a colour TV receiver. For clarity, the time base and sound channels are not shown since they are identical to the monochrome receiver. The modulated carrier is received and detected by the a.m. detector. The video signal reproduced by the a.m. detector contains two components: the monochrome or luminance (Y) and the colour content or chrominance. The luminance is amplified separately and fed into the decoder. The decoder contains a chrominance amplifier, detector and matrix. It receives both the luminance and chrominance signals and converts them back to R, G, B signals, which are amplified separately and fed into the CRT.

The shadow mask tube (Fig. 16.9)

This is one type of cathode ray tube used by British manufacturers for colour TV receivers. Three identical guns are used, fed with R, G and B signals. The guns are mounted at 120° to each other at the neck of the tube and scan the screen simultaneously. The colour is created at the screen by focussing each gun on a specially coated dot which when hit by a fast electron emits a primary colour.

These dots are arranged to form a regular system of triangles (RGB). To ensure that each gun hits its particular dot and no other, a 'shadow mask' is used. The dots are indistinguishable to the naked eye which sees the three colours mixed together, recreating the original coloured picture. Convergence coils fed with line and field pulses placed on the neck of the tube ensure that the three guns scan the same line.

Fig. 16.9 The shadow mask tube

Electron guns

Deflecting coils

Shadow mask

Screen

B
G
R

R
G
B

Precision-in-line tube

A modern tube is the precision in-line (PIL) (Fig. 16.10) with the three guns mounted in the same horizontal plane.

Converge problems are easier to overcome with this type of tube. This is because the amount of vertical deflection is the same for all three guns. Only the horizontal movement is assymetrical for the three guns. The phosphors on the screen are in similar configuration to the guns. Instead of the dots in the delta type, the PIL tube has vertical stripes of phosphors as shown in Fig. 16.10.

In-line guns

Blue

Green

Red

Shadow mask

Screen

Blue Green Red

Green

Primary colour phosphor stripes

Blue Red

Fig. 16.10

17 Digital gates and system

Fig. 17.1 The AND gate

Fig. 17.2 Two-input NAND gate

Digital control is a relatively new area in electronics which developed from the science of telecommunication. Digital control embraces computers, electronic telephone exchanges, industrial control systems, data processing, and other similar systems. Digital devices function in discrete steps, usually ON or OFF. The essential requirement of a digital device is that it should change from one state to another without settling in any intermediate position.

Gates

Gates are logic or digital devices that give a 2-state output: a zero output (indicated by 0) and a fixed output (indicated by 1). A gate can have several inputs but produces only one output.

AND

The AND gate produces an output of 1 when all its inputs are 1. Figure 17.1 shows an AND gate with two inputs. Only when both input A and B are 1 does the output become 1. Table 17.1 shows what is known as the **truth table** for the AND gate.

Table 17.1 AND

Input		Output
A	B	
0	0	0
0	1	0
1	0	0
1	1	1

NAND (Fig. 17.2)

The NAND gate gives a 0 output when all its inputs are 1. Conversely, if a 0 is present at any of its inputs, the output will be 1.

Table 17.2 NAND

Input		Output
A	B	
0	0	1
0	1	1
1	0	1
1	1	0

The NAND gate is thus the opposite of the AND gate. Table 17.2 is the truth table.

OR (Fig. 17.3)

The OR gate gives a 1 output if any of its inputs are 1. Conversely, it requires a 0 on each input for it to give an output of 0. Table 17.3 is the truth table.

Fig. 17.3   Two-input OR gate

Table 17.3   OR

Input		Output
A	B	
0	0	0
0	1	1
1	0	1
1	1	1

NOR (Fig. 17.4)

The NOR gate gives a 0 output if any of its inputs is 1. Conversely, it requires a 0 on each of its inputs to give a 1 output. The NOR gate is thus opposite to the OR gate. Table 17.4 is the truth table.

Fig. 17.4   Two-input NOR gate

Table 17.4   NOR

Input		Output
A	B	
0	0	1
0	1	0
1	0	0
1	1	0

Fig. 17.5   NOT gate

NOT (Fig. 17.5)

The NOT gate is an invertor. When the input is 1, the output is 0, and vice versa. Table 17.5 is the truth table.

Table 17.5   NOT

Input	Output
0	1
1	0

Fig. 17.6

Exclusive-OR (Fig. 17.6)

The Exclusive-OR (Ex-OR) gate gives an output of 1 when either of its inputs is 1 but not when both inputs are at either logic 1 or logic 0. The truth table is shown in Table 17.6.

Table 17.6   Ex-OR

Input		Output
A	B	
0	0	0
0	1	1
1	0	1
1	1	0

US symbols

The gate symbols shown are those recommended by British Standards. However, many manufacturers use the US symbols as shown in Fig. 17.7. In this book, we will use both symbols. A summary of the truth tables is shown in Table 17.7.

Table 17.7

Inputs						
A	B	AND	OR	NAND	NOR	Exclusive-OR
0	0	0	0	1	1	0
0	1	0	1	1	0	1
1	0	0	1	1	0	1
1	1	1	1	0	0	0

Fig. 17.7

Combinational gates

Digital systems usually involve more than one gate combined together to give the required control. For instance, a simple combination of an AND gate with a NOT gate (Fig. 17.8(a)) functions the same way as a NAND gate.

Similarly, a NOR gate can be constructed by an OR gate and a NOT gate as shown in Fig. 17.8(b).

As a further example, the input to the logic circuit shown in Fig. 17.9 is 0111; the question is to find the output.

Output of OR gate (i) is 1. Output of NAND gate (ii) is 0, giving an input to OR gate (iii) of 10 for an output at G of 1.

Fig. 17.8

Boolean expressions

The functions of the individual gates or combinations of gates may be expressed in a logical statement known as a Boolean expression. Boolean algebra uses the following notations:

1. The AND function is represented by the dot symbol (.). Thus a 2-input (A,B) AND gate has an output represented by the Boolean expression A.B.
2. The OR function is represented by the plus symbol (+). Thus a 2-input OR gate has an output represented by A + B.
3. The NOT function is represented by a bar over the input. Thus a NOT gate with input A has an output represented by $\overline{A}$ (read as NOT A).

From the above, it follows that:

the NOR function is expressed by $\overline{A+B}$ (NOT-OR)
and the NAND function is expressed by $\overline{A.B}$ (NOT-AND)

EXAMPLE 1

Consider the combinational logic circuit shown in Fig. 17.9 and reproduced in Fig. 17.10 using US symbols. The function of the circuit may be worked out using the Boolean expressions as follows:

Output of OR gate (i) is $A + B$
Output of NAND gate (ii) is $\overline{C.D}$

∴ Output of OR gate (iii) is $(A + B) + (\overline{C.D})$

Fig. 17.10

The binary system

While the decimal or denary system of counting uses ten different digits, the binary system uses two digits only, zero and one (0 and 1). This system fits in with the logic gates just dealt with.

In the decimal system, the first column A (Table 17.8) is the ones or units column, column B is the tens, C is the hundreds, D is the thousands, and so on. In the binary system each column can either be 0 or 1 with the first column A corresponding to the ones, column B to the twos, column C to the fours, D to the eights, and so on. Any number can be written in the decimal as well as the binary system. Table 17.9 shows the conversion into binary of the decimal numbers nought to seven.

Table 17.8

Decimal columns					Binary columns			
D	C	B	A		D	C	B	A
10^3	10^2	10^1	10^0		2^3	2^2	2^1	2^0
1000s	100s	tens	units		eights	fours	twos	units

Table 17.9

Decimal	Binary		
	C (4)	B (2)	A (1)
0	0	0	0
1	0	0	1
2	0	1	0
3	0	1	1
4	1	0	0
5	1	0	1
6	1	1	0
7	1	1	1

Table 17.10

Binary	Binary columns						Decimals
	32	16	8	4	2	1	
1110	—	—	1	1	1	0	= 8+4+2 = 14
1011	—	—	1	0	1	1	= 8+2+1 = 11
11001	—	1	1	0	0	1	= 16+8+1 = 25
10111	—	1	0	1	1	1	= 16+4+2+1 = 23
110010	1	1	0	0	1	0	= 32+16+2 = 50

For numbers higher than seven, a fourth column (the eights) is needed. Thus 8 = 1000, 9 = 1001, 10 = 1010, 11 = 1011 and so on.

Table 17.10 shows some examples of conversion from binary into decimal.

Frequency counter

An AND gate in conjunction with a counter can be used to measure frequency or time period. Figure 17.11 shows a 2-input AND gate together with a counter used as a frequency meter.

Fig. 17.11 AND gate as frequency meter

Input A is fed with the input signal. Input B is fed with a timing pulse of predetermined duration. At the output of the gate, the signal pulses will be present only for the duration of the timing pulse. These pulses are then fed into the counter which counts them, giving the frequency of the input signal. For example, if the timing pulse was of 10 ms duration and the frequency of the input was 1 kHz giving a periodic time of 1 ms, then only 10 pulses will appear at the output of the AND gate to be counted by the counter giving a reading of 1.0 kHz.

Digital clock

A crystal oscillator with very high stability is used to feed a chain of frequency dividers to produce accurate timing pulses. The decoders convert the timing pulses from the dividers into suitable signals to operate the display units (see also Chapter 34). The seconds display is fed with the highest frequency and the hours display with the lowest frequency.

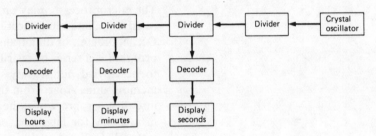

Fig. 17.12 Digital clock system

18 Microcomputers and other systems

Computer system

Figure 18.1 shows a basic computer system. The 'brain' of the computer is the microprocessor which carries out the arithmetic and logical operations as well as controlling the whole system. The microprocessor may carry out mathematical operations such as addition and multiplication, logical operations such as AND, OR, NOR etc., or data transfer as instructed by a program. The program is a series of instructions which sets out the operations to be carried out step-by-step. The program is stored in the memory unit. Apart from the program which the memory feeds into the microprocessor, the microprocessor may store some data in memory for later use, e.g. temperature readings at regular intervals for later analysis, or sales figures of a certain item for later comparison with other items. Communication between the microprocessor and the memory, therefore, may take place in both directions, as shown. Such communication is known as *bidirectional*.

Fig. 18.1

The microprocessor also controls the whole system in terms of timing each step, synchronising the operation of each unit, activating the necessary units and directing the data around the system.

The microprocessor receives input data such as temperature readings, sales or other relevant information as required by the particular program via input devices such as a temperature sensing device or a keyboard. It communicates the results of the program to the outside world via output devices such as a printer or a visual display unit (VDU).

Interface unit

In most applications, direct connection between one part of a system and another is not possible. The signals may be incompatible, requiring conversion (e.g. analogue-to-digital) or conditioning (e.g. attenuation or amplification). To overcome this, an interface is employed between one unit and another, as shown in Fig. 18.2. The interface may be an analogue-to-digital converter, a transducer, an attenuator, or a simple adapter.

Fig. 18.2

Figure 18.3 shows a complete microprocessor-based computer, also known as microcomputer, including the necessary interface units. Communication to and from the microprocessor is in the form of multi-line parallel connectors carrying digital information in the form of binary numbers. The numbers of parallel lines may be 8, 16 or 32. These parallel connectors are grouped together to form a multi-line **bus**. In most microcomputer

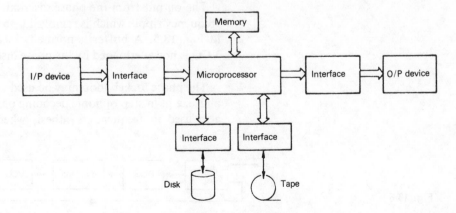

Fig. 18.3

systems, peripheral (external) memory stores are used to feed a program or part of a program (sub-routine) into the microprocessor, to supply information (data), or to store information from the microprocessor. Hence, the bidirectional communication. Such peripheral devices include a tape recorder and a disc which may be used as memory stores to supplement the memory unit of the system.

The phase locked loop

In many applications, phase locking of signals is essential. Phase locking is the process of producing a signal which is in phase with another reference frequency. The phase locked loop (Fig. 18.4) is such a phase locking device.

Fig. 18.4

The main elements of a phase locked loop are the phase discriminator and the voltage controlled oscillator (VCO). The phase discriminator has two inputs and a d.c. output. The d.c. output is determined by the phase difference of the two inputs. The VCO produces a sinusoidal output whose frequency is determined by the level of the d.c. input going into it.

Referring to Fig. 18.4, the output from the VCO is fed back to the phase discriminator. A difference in phase between the fed-back signal B and the reference input A produces a d.c. voltage which is amplified before going into the VCO to adjust its frequency. This continues until the fed-back signal B and the reference input A are in phase.

The output from the phase discriminator contains some high frequency ripple which is removed by a low pass filter, as shown in Fig. 18.5. A buffer is normally included to ensure that the VCO is not overloaded by the phase discriminator or any output load.

The phase locked loop may be used as an oscillator with fixed phase, e.g. in stereophonic decoding or a frequency divider. It is also used in frequency synthesis where sinusoidal signals are

Fig. 18.5

made up from a central signal and for frequency measurement in control processes.

Speed control system

Figure 18.6 shows a block diagram for a speed control system.

Fig. 18.6

D.C. control voltage

The purpose of the system is to set the speed of the d.c. motor and keep it constant at that speed. The motor speed is set by the block labelled 'set speed control'. The motor is driven by the d.c. power amplifier. The motor itself drives a d.c. generator, the output of which is determined by the speed of the motor. The output of the d.c. generator is fed back into a differential or difference amplifier. The difference amplifier has two inputs going into it. One input comes from the speed control and the other from the d.c. generator. The difference amplifier compares the two inputs and produces an output which is proportional to the difference between the two inputs. If the motor is running fast, the d.c. control voltage from the d.c. generator is high. The difference between this voltage and the other input to the difference amplifier is therefore reduced. A smaller voltage is therefore obtained from the difference amplifier, reducing the speed of the motor back to its original level. A slow-running motor will produce the opposite effect.

Magnetic tape recorder

In the tape recorder, audio information is converted into a changing magnetic field across a very small gap in a recording head. The changing magnetic field is transformed into a magnetic pattern on a magnetic tape passing along the gap at constant speed. When the tape is played back, the magnetic pattern on the tape is transformed back into a changing magnetic field and subsequently into an audio signal. The recording head itself may be used for playback.

A straightforward magnetisation of the tape introduces non-linearity. To overcome this the audio signal is superimposed on a constant high-frequency signal of between 30 to 100 kHz, referred to as h.f. bias. This high-frequency bias is also used to erase the recording. An erasing head is placed ahead of the recording head which is switched on only when the machine is on record.

Figure 18.7 shows a block diagram of a tape recorder. When switched to playback (a transducer in this case), the playback head converts the magnetic information on the tape into an audio signal. The audio signal is amplified by a pre-amp and fed into a power output stage before going into the loudspeaker. On record, both the record and the erase heads are activated. The audio information from the microphone is amplified before going into a transducer (the record head) to convert it into a changing magnetic field. The erase head ensures that the tape is clean of any magnetic information (before new signals are recorded).

Fig. 18.7

19 The semiconductor diode

Conductors and insulators

All substances are made up of one or more chemical elements such as oxygen, sulphur, etc. The smallest part of an element is the atom. Atoms of different elements may combine to form a molecule of a substance, e.g. a molecule of water comprises two atoms of hydrogen and one atom of oxygen. In this way different substances are made up.

The atom itself is composed of smaller particles known as electrons revolving around a central nucleus containing one or more protons and neutrons (Fig. 19.1). The electrons which are negatively charged are attracted to the positive protons and continuously rotate in orbits or shells round the nucleus. The number of electrons in an atom is exactly balanced by the number of protons.

Fig. 19.1 Atoms consist of negative electrons rotating round a positive nucleus

Atoms of different elements are differentiated one from the other by the number of electrons it contains, e.g. a hydrogen atom has one electron while that of carbon has six. For electrical conduction to occur, electrons which are loosely connected to the nucleus (known as free electrons) leave their orbit when attracted by a positive potential, and begin to travel along forming a flow of electrons, or current.

A good conductor has a large number of 'loose' or free electrons. These free electrons will aid the flow of current. A good conductor will have such a small resistance that it can be neglected — examples are silver, copper and aluminium.

An insulator is a material with very few free electrons. Insulators restrict the flow of current very heavily and thus have very large resistances approaching an open circuit. Examples are glass, dry wood, rubber, p.v.c., mica and polystyrene.

Fig. 19.2 Conductors, semiconductors and insulators

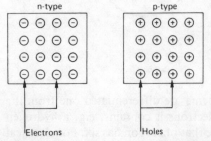

Fig. 19.3 n-type and p-type semiconductors

Semiconductors

Semiconductors have their atoms grouped together in a regular pattern called a 'crystal lattice'. They are not good conductors (hence their name) since they have few 'free electrons'. The number of 'free electrons' increases as the temperature goes up, which leads to improved conductivity. These 'free electrons' are known as minority carriers.

Conductivity may also be improved by adding controlled amounts of 'impurities'. Impurities such as arsenic atoms introduce extra electrons in the lattice structure producing the n-type semiconductor. Such atoms are known as *donor* atoms. On the other hand impurity atoms known as *acceptor* atoms, for instance aluminium atoms, introduce a 'shortage of electrons' referred to as holes and producing the p-type semiconductor (Fig. 19.3). The electrons and holes produced by the injection of impurities are known as the majority carriers.

The junction diode

When a p-type semiconductor is joined to an n-type semi-conductor (Fig. 19.4), by a process known as *diffusion*, electrons from the n-region begin to cross over to fill the holes in the p-region. This movement continues until a neutral zone known as the *depletion layer* is established on either side of the pn junction. This depletion layer provides a potential barrier preventing further movement by electrons across the junction.

Electrons wishing to cross over must now have sufficient energy to overcome the potential barrier. Such energy may be provided by an external e.m.f. The height of the potential barrier depends on the semiconductor used, namely 0.3 V for Germanium (Ge) and 0.6 V for Silicon (Si).

Fig. 19.4   The pn junction diode

Diode characteristics

When the diode is reverse biased (Fig. 19.5), electrons in the n-region are attracted to the positive electrode of the bias voltage, while the holes in the p-region are attracted to the negative electrode. The depletion layer is thus widened, producing a higher potential barrier resisting further the flow of electrons.

Fig. 19.5 Reverse biased diode. (a) Shows the increase in the width of the depletion layer

A forward bias, however, removes the depletion layer as shown in Fig. 19.6, allowing the electrons to cross over, with current due to majority carriers flowing freely. However, the diode maintains a constant voltage drop across it known as the forward voltage drop (0.3 V for Ge and 0.6 V for Si diodes).

The junction diode forward characteristics are as shown in Fig. 19.7. Note that as soon as the bias voltage overcomes the potential barrier of the diode, a large current begins to flow. A *very small* increase in the bias voltage produces a *very large* increase in the current through the diode. For bias voltages below the required forward voltage drop, a small leakage current (in microamps) flows which is usually neglected.

Fig. 19.6 Forward biased diode. (a) shows the elimination of the depletion layer

(a)

(b)

Fig. 19.7 Forward characteristics of germanium and silicon diodes

Fig. 19.8 Reverse characteristics of a junction diode

The reverse bias characteristics are as shown in Fig. 19.8. An extremely small current passes through the diode when in reverse bias, due to minority carriers. This reverse current is almost constant up to a maximum voltage known as the reverse breakdown voltage. If a higher voltage is applied, breakdown occurs and the reverse current increases rapidly causing damage to the diode. Care must always be taken to ensure that diodes are not subjected to reverse voltages higher than the breakdown voltage specified by the manufacturer. Germanium diodes have higher leakage currents and therefore lower reverse resistance than silicon diodes.

20 Transistors

The transistor is a semiconductor device made up of two pn junctions as shown in Fig. 20.1. There are three terminals to the transistor, known as the emitter, base, and collector. Transistors may be of two types: the pnp shown in (a) and the npn shown in (b). The principle of operation for both types is the same, the difference being in the d.c. bias conditions.

Fig. 20.1 (a) pnp transistor with its symbol (b) npn transistor with its symbol

Fig. 20.2 Bias voltages for npn transistor

Consider the npn transistor shown in Fig. 20.2. The base–emitter (b–e) junction is forward biased by voltage V_2. Electrons from the emitter (I_e) will, therefore, flow across the junction from emitter to base. It is the normal forward current for a forward bias pn junction. As soon as the electrons cross over into the base, they are attracted by the positive potential of the collector. By making the base region very thin it is possible to have almost all of these electrons move across the base region towards the collector. Only a very small number of electrons is collected by the base forming the base current I_b. In fact 95% or more of the emitter current I_e is now collected by the collector to form the collector current I_c. Therefore,

$$I_e = I_c + I_b$$

Since base current I_b is very small (in μA) it is usually neglected. I_c and I_e are assumed to be equal and are generally referred to as the transistor current.

109

Fig. 20.3 Bias voltages for pnp transistor

It will be noticed that the base–collector (b–c) junction is reversed biased by voltage V_{CB}. This is essential otherwise the electrons will not be attracted towards the collector. Conventional flow of current from positive to negative will show transistor current flowing from collector to emitter.

For a pnp transistor the polarities of the d.c. supplies must be reversed as shown in Fig. 20.3. In this case the transistor current is a movement of holes from emitter to collector or electrons from collector to emitter.

Transistor configurations

There are three possible ways to connect a transistor when used in a circuit.

Fig. 20.4 Common emitter (CE) configuration

1. The **common emitter** (CE) configuration where the input signal is fed between the base and emitter, while the output is taken between collector and emitter (Fig. 20.4). This is the most widely used configuration due to its flexibility and high gain.

2. The **common base** (CB) configuration where the base is common to both input and output (Fig. 20.5).

3. The **common collector** (CC) configuration where the collector is common. This configuration is also known as the emitter follower (Fig. 20.6).

Fig. 20.5 Common base (CB) configuration

While the internal behaviour is exactly the same for each configuration, external behaviour is different for each case. Each configuration presents different characteristics in terms of its gain, input and output impedances and frequency response.

Common emitter characteristic curves

The transistor has three types of characteristic curve outlining its behaviour under static (or quiescent) conditions, i.e. with no input signal. These are:

Fig. 20.6 Common collector (CC) configuration (Note that the output is taken from the emitter)

1. The **input characteristics**, the graph of *input* current against *input* voltage.

2. The **output characteristics**, the graph of *output* current against *output* voltage.

3. The **transfer characteristics**, the graph of *output* current against *input* current.

The characteristics described below are for an npn transistor (Fig. 20.7). For a pnp transistor the d.c. voltages should be negative.

Fig. 20.7

Input characteristics

Figure 20.8 shows the input characteristics for an npn transistor.

Fig. 20.8 Input characteristics of a transistor

It is the same as the characteristics of a forward biased pn junction since the input (b−e) is a forward biased junction. It will be noted that just as in the case of a junction diode, the input current I_b flows only when the required forward voltage drop is established across the b−e junction. Once that voltage (0.3 V for Ge and 0.6 V for Si) is established, the voltage between base and emitter V_{be} remains practically constant for a large increase of base current. Hence the transistor is considered as a current device, i.e. a varying input current with a constant input voltage.

Output characteristics

Figure 20.9 shows a family of curves known as the output characteristics relating collector or output current I_c to collector or output voltage V_{CE} for specific values of base or input current I_b. These curves also provide a relationship between the input current on the one hand and output current and voltage on the other. For example, given a transistor with a base current of 40 μA and a collector voltage of 6 V, then using the output characteristics in Fig. 20.9 a collector current of 4 mA will be flowing.

The curve $I_b = 0$ represents the state of the transistor before it begins to conduct, i.e. at cut-off when V_{be} is below the required forward voltage drop. Theoretically, transistor current is zero when $I_b = 0$; however, a small leakage current does flow through to the collector.

Fig. 20.9 Output characteristics of a transistor

Static current gain h_{fe}

A very important parameter of any transistor is its d.c. current gain, known as the static current gain h_{fe}. It is the current gain of the transistor at quiescence, i.e. without an input signal. It has no units (it is a ratio).

$$\text{Static current gain } h_{fe} = \frac{\text{Output current}}{\text{Input current}} = \frac{I_c}{I_b}$$

h_{fe} can be calculated from the output characteristics. For example, if the transistor is operating at point Q where $I_b = 40\ \mu\text{A}$, and $I_c = 4\ \text{mA}$ then

$$h_{fe} = \frac{I_c}{I_b} = \frac{4 \times 1000}{40} = 100$$

Transfer characteristics

These are the relationship between the input and output currents (Fig. 20.10). The static current gain may also be calculated using this characteristic curve. For example, if Q is the operating point of the transistor then

$$h_{fe} = \frac{I_c}{I_b} = \frac{4 \times 1000}{40} = 100$$

Fig. 20.10 Transfer (or mutual) characteristics of a transistor

21 The common emitter amplifier

(a)

(b)

Fig. 21.1 Base bias for npn transistor

Before the transistor can be used as an amplifier it must have the correct d.c. bias, as shown in Fig. 21.1(a) for an npn transistor. It can be seen that the two voltages V_{BE} (providing the forward bias for the b–e junction) and V_{CB} (providing the reverse bias for the b–c junction) are connected in series. V_{BE} and V_{CB} can thus be substituted by the potential divider R_1–R_2 shown in Fig. 21.1b. This way only one d.c. supply voltage is required, namely V_{cc}. The ratio of R_1 to R_2 is chosen so that the transistor is given the required bias at the base.

A standing current $I_s = V_{cc}/(R_1 + R_2)$ flows through the bias chain R_1–R_2 causing a drain on the supply voltage. To reduce this standing current, high values of R_1 and R_2 are used. However, as will be seen later, a very high value of R_1 reduces the d.c. stability of the transistor.

The voltage at the base is the voltage between the base and the 0 V line or chassis, i.e. the voltage across resistor R_2.

$$\text{Voltage at the base } V_b = V_{R_2} = \frac{V_{cc}}{R_1 + R_2} \times R_2.$$

For example, given $V_{cc} = 10$ V, $R_1 = 15$ kΩ, $R_2 = 1$ kΩ, then

$$V_b = \frac{V_{cc}}{R_1 + R_2} \times R_2 = \frac{10 \text{ V}}{15 \text{ kΩ} + 1 \text{ kΩ}} \times 1 \text{ kΩ}$$

$$= \frac{10}{16} \times 1 = 0.625 \text{ V}$$

By using different values of R_1, R_2 or both, the base voltage may be varied.

The same biasing arrangement may be used for a pnp transistor as shown in Fig. 21.2. In this case the d.c. supply is negative, $-V_{cc}$. The function of bias chain R_1–R_2 is the same as that for the npn transistor. The fact that the d.c. voltages are

113

Fig. 21.2 Base bias for pnp transistor

negative should be remembered but need not be included in calculation. Hence

$$V_b = \frac{V_{cc}}{R_1 + R_2} \times R_2 = \frac{10}{15+1} \times 1 = \frac{10}{16} = 0.625 \text{ V}$$

The voltage at the base is -0.625 V.

For a forward bias to be established across the b–e junction, the base voltage has to be 'higher' than the emitter voltage; 'higher', whether in the positive (npn) or in the negative (pnp) directions. In general, regardless of the type of transistor used, the base voltage is always higher than the emitter but lower than the collector.

As explained in the previous section, the current through the transistor is determined by the b–e forward bias V_{be}, i.e. the potential difference between base and emitter $V_{be} = V_b - V_e$. A variation in emitter or base voltage causes a change in transistor current. In the transistor circuit under consideration the emitter being at chassis potential, only the base can change with

$$V_{be} = 0.62 - 0 = 0.62 \text{ V}$$

For example, if the base voltage V_b goes away from the emitter (more positive for npn or more negative for pnp transistors), V_{be} increases causing the transistor current to go up. On the other hand if V_b goes towards the emitter, V_{be} decreases and the transistor current is reduced.

Collector or load resistor

In order to produce an output voltage at the collector, a load resistor R_3 (also known as the collector resistor) is added as shown in Fig. 21.3. The collector current I_c flows through collector resistor R_3 developing a voltage across it. Hence

$$V_{R_3} = I_c \times R_3$$

Fig. 21.3 The load resistor R_3

Since all voltages are measured with respect to chassis or earth potential, the collector voltage V_{ce} is the p.d. between the collector and the chassis. As can be seen from the circuit,

Supply voltage $V_{cc} = V_{R_3} + V_{ce}$

Hence $V_{ce} = V_{cc} - V_{R_3}$
Taking the typical values shown where $I_c = 1.2$ mA,

$$V_{R_3} = I_c \times R_3 = 1.2 \text{ mA} \times 3.3 \text{ k}\Omega = 4 \text{ V (approx.)}$$
$$V_{ce} = V_{cc} - V_{R_3} = 10 - 4 = 6 \text{ V}$$

Thermal runaway

It has been mentioned in Chapter 19 that minority carriers form what is known as leakage current across a reverse biased junction. A leakage current I_{CEO} will, therefore, flow across the reverse biased base–collector junction as shown in Fig. 21.4. It is amplified in the same way as the input (or base) current by a factor of h_{fe}. As the temperature of the transistor increases, so the leakage current goes up. This is amplified by the transistor, increasing the collector current which in turn raises the temperature further, causing the leakage current to go up, and so on. The process known as thermal runaway is cumulative and if unchecked could cause damage to the transistor.

Fig. 21.4 Leakage current I_{CEO}

D.C. stabilisation

The effect of leakage current in the CE amplifier is to cause instability in d.c. or static operating conditions. This can be overcome by the addition of emitter resistor R_4 as shown in Fig. 21.5. The emitter voltage is now equal to the volt drop produced by the emitter current I_e flowing through emitter resistor R_4. Hence $V_e = I_e \times R_4$. D.C. stabilisation takes place as follows.

If I_c and I_e increase due to an increase in leakage current, the emitter voltage V_e increases with it. Since $V_{be} = V_b - V_e$ then an increase in V_e produces a decrease in V_{be}. This reduces the base current and restores I_c and I_e to their previous values. The emitter resistor R_4 provides a negative feedback loop giving stability to the static conditions of the amplifier. Using the typical values given in Fig. 21.5 and assuming emitter current $I_e = 1.2$ mA, then $V_e = I_e \times R_4 = 1.2 \text{ mA} \times 1 \text{ k}\Omega = 1.2 \text{ V}$.

Fig. 21.5 npn common emitter amplifier with emitter resistor R_4

$$V_b = \frac{V_{cc}}{R_1 + R_2} \times R_2 = \frac{10}{15 \text{ k}\Omega + 3.3 \text{ k}\Omega} \times 3.3 \text{ k}\Omega$$

$$= \frac{10}{18.3} \times 3.3 = 1.8 \text{ V}$$

$$V_{be} = V_b - V_e = 1.8 - 1.2 = 0.6 \text{ V}$$

Fig. 21.6 pnp common emitter amplifier

Using pnp transistors

Figure 21.6 shows a pnp transistor amplifier. Assuming the transistor to be silicon, its current, emitter, base and collector voltages can be calculated as follows:

$$V_b = \frac{V_{cc}}{R_1 + R_2} \times R_2 = \frac{10}{22 \text{ k}\Omega + 3.9 \text{ k}\Omega} \times 3.9 \text{ k}\Omega$$

$$= \frac{10}{25.9} \times 3.9 = 1.5 \text{ V}$$

From $V_{be} = V_b - V_e$ we get $V_e = V_b - V_{be}$ but $V_{be} = 0.6$ V (silicon transistor) and $V_b = 1.5$ V. Therefore

$$V_e = 1.5 - 0.6 = 0.9 \text{ V}$$

From $V_e = I_e \times R_4$, we get

$$I_e = \frac{V_e}{R_4} = \frac{0.9 \text{ V}}{820 \text{ }\Omega} = \frac{0.9 \text{ V}}{0.82 \text{ k}\Omega} = 1.1 \text{ mA}$$

$$I_c = I_e = 1.1 \text{ mA}$$
$$V_{R_3} = I_c \times R_3 = 1.1 \text{ mA} \times 3.3 \text{ k}\Omega = 3.6 \text{ V}$$
$$V_c = V_{cc} - V_{R_3} = 10 - 3.6 = 6.4 \text{ V}$$

The static operating conditions of the transistor are therefore

$$e - 0.9 \text{ V}, \quad b - 1.5 \text{ V}, \quad c - 6.4 \text{ V} \quad \text{with} \quad I_e = 1.1 \text{ mA}$$

The emitter, base and collector voltages given above are typical for a single stage amplifier such as an i.f. amplifier or a driver. The emitter is approximately $0.1 \times V_{cc}$, with the collector at approximately $0.6 \times V_{cc}$. It can be seen that for both types of transistor the emitter voltage is lowest while that of the collector is highest, with the base at approximately 0.6 V (for Si transistors) above the emitter.

The npn transistor with negative supply

It is possible to connect an npn transistor using a negative d.c. supply voltage $-V_{cc}$ as shown in Fig. 21.7. In this case the chassis is the positive rail. All voltages are, therefore, negative as they are all measured with respect to the positive chassis. Using the typical values given in the diagram we get

$$V_b = \text{voltage across } R_1 = \frac{V_{cc}}{R_1 + R_2} \times R_1$$

Fig. 21.7 npn transistor amplifier using negative supply $- V_{cc}$

$$= \frac{10}{15 + 3.3} \times 15 = \frac{10}{18.3} \times 15 = 8.2 \text{ V}$$

$$V_c = \text{voltage across } R_3 = I_c \times R_3 = 1.2 \text{ mA} \times 3.3 \text{ k}\Omega$$
$$= 4 \text{ V (approx.)}$$
$$V_e = V_{cc} - V_{R_4} = V_{cc} - I_e \times R_4 = 10 - 1.2 \times 1$$
$$= 10 - 1.2 = 8.8 \text{ V.}$$

The static operating condition of the transistor is therefore: $e - 8.8$ V, $b - 8.2$ V, $c - 4$ V.

Base current

Fig. 21.8 The effect of base current I_b

Base current I_b (Fig. 21.8) flows from the positive d.c. rail through R_1 across the b—e junction to the emitter. Bias resistor R_1 thus has two currents flowing through it: standing current I_s (which also flows through R_2) plus the base current I_b (which does not flow through R_2). The volt drop across R_1 thus increases by $I_b \times R_1$. Since $V_{R_1} + V_{R_2} = V_{cc}$ then an increase in V_{R_1} would result in an equal decrease in V_{R_2}, i.e. a drop in base voltage. Under normal circumstances I_b is very small and may be neglected with V_b assumed to be determined by resistor chain $R_1 - R_2$.

However, if the base current is large (e.g. when a transistor is conducting very heavily) or if R_1 is made very large, the change in base voltage due to I_b begins to affect the static conditions of the transistor and has to be taken into account.

Consider the circuit in Fig. 21.8. Under normal conditions a base current of say 10 µA produces a voltage drop across R_1 of $I_b \times R_1 = 10 \times 10^{-6} \times 15 \times 10^3 = 150 \times 10^{-3} = 0.15$ V which is small compared with a base voltage of 1.8 V determined by bias chain $R_1 - R_2$. If the transistor is now made to conduct very heavily, taking a large current, base current will also be high, say 80 µA. Voltage across R_1 due to 80 µA base current is $80 \times 10^{-6} \times 15 \times 10^3 = 80 \times 15 \times 10^{-3} = 1.2$ V. The base voltage will drop by an equal amount, i.e. from 1.8 V to 0.6 V.

Base current biasing

Fig. 21.9 Base current biasing

The base current can be used to provide the normal bias for a transistor as shown in Fig. 21.9. In this circuit R_2 is dispensed with and a very large R_1 is used. Current I_b is now entirely responsible for the volt drop across R_1 (there is no standing current). This volt drop is large enough to provide the normal bias.

Given that the base current in Fig. 21.9 is 10 µA the base voltage may be calculated as follows:

$$V_{R_1} = I_b \times R_1 = 10 \times 10^{-6} \times 390 \times 10^3 = 3900 \times 10^{-3}$$
$$= 3.9 \text{ V}$$

The voltage at the base is the voltage between the base and chassis, i.e.

Fig. 21.10 Cut-off condition: $V_e = 0$ V, $V_c = V_{cc}$

Fig. 21.11 Saturation condition: $V_e \cong V_c$

$$V_b = V_{cc} - V_{R_1} = 6 - 3.9 = 2.1 \text{ V}$$

The circuit in Fig. 21.9 has the advantage of having a higher input impedance due to the absence of the input shunting resistor R_2 but it has no d.c. stability.

Cut-off and saturation

A transistor is said to be at cut-off when it ceases to conduct, i.e. its current is zero. With $I_e = 0$, no voltage is developed across R_4 (Fig. 21.10). Hence the emitter voltage ($V_e = I_e \times R_4$) is also zero. A zero collector current produces no p.d. across R_3 ($V_{R_3} = I_c \times R_3$) making the collector go to the supply V_{cc}. Voltage between collector and emitter $V_{CE} (= V_c - V_e)$ is, therefore, equal to V_{cc}.

A transistor is said to be saturated when the current through it is so high that it cannot increase any further, i.e. when I_e and I_c are at their maximum value. As I_e increases, V_e also increases (Fig. 21.11). The voltage across R_3 increases as I_c increases, forcing the collector to go away from V_{cc} towards the emitter ($V_c = V_{cc} - V_{R_3}$). Hence as the current through the transistor increases, the emitter voltage goes towards the collector while the collector goes towards the emitter. At saturation, when the transistor current is at a maximum, V_e and V_c are approximately equal, with V_{CE} almost at zero. Figure 21.11 gives typical values for saturation.

22 Common emitter amplifier – a.c. operation

Coupling capacitor

The purpose of a.c. coupling is to block the d.c. while allowing the a.c. signal through. Such coupling devices, e.g. a capacitor or a transformer, are usually used at the input and output of an amplifier. The quiescent or d.c. conditions of the transistor are thus not affected by the preceding or succeeding stages.

Figure 22.1 shows capacitor C coupling point A to point B with R as the load resistor. As far as d.c. is concerned, the capacitor acts as an open circuit blocking the d.c. between A and B. For this reason a coupling capacitor is also known as a *blocking capacitor*.

Fig. 22.1 Capacitor coupling

For satisfactory a.c. coupling, the capacitor must have a reactance X_c at the operating frequency which is very small as compared with the value of the load resistor R so that a very small fraction of the input signal is dropped across C. For instance if V_1 = 100 mV, then satisfactory coupling may be said to be achieved if the output V_o = 95 mV, a drop of 5 mV (5%) due to the coupling capacitor.

The value of a coupling capacitor depends on two factors.

1. Load resistor R. Assuming that satisfactory coupling is achieved when $X_c = R/20$ and given that $R = 1 \text{ k}\Omega$ and the operating frequency $f = 300$ Hz then,

$$X_c = \frac{1}{20} R = \frac{1}{20} \times 1000 = 50 \ \Omega$$

From $X_c = 1/2\pi f C_1$, we get

$$C_1 = \frac{1}{2\pi f X_c} = \frac{1}{2\pi \times 300 \times 50} = 10.6 \ \mu F \ \text{or} \ 10 \ \mu F$$

approx.

If the load resistor is increased to 100 kΩ,

$$X_c = \frac{1}{20} R = \frac{1}{20} \times 100 \ k\Omega = 5 \ k\Omega$$

$$C_2 = \frac{1}{2\pi f X_c} = \frac{1}{2\pi \times 300 \times 5 \times 10^3} = 0.1 \ \mu F$$

Hence if the load resistor is increased by 100 times (from 1 kΩ to 100 kΩ), the coupling capacitor may be decreased by the same proportion (from 10 μF to 0.1 μF).

In general the higher the load resistor, the smaller the required value of the coupling capacitor.

2. The frequency of operation. Take the above example where satisfactory coupling was achieved when $C = 10 \ \mu F$ and $R = 1 \ k\Omega$ with $f = 300$ Hz.

If the frequency is now increased to 300 kHz then with $X_c = R/20 = 50 \ \Omega$

$$C_3 = \frac{1}{2\pi f X_c} = \frac{1}{2\pi \times 300 \times 10^3 \times 50} = 0.01 \ \mu F$$

Hence if the frequency is increased by 1000 times (from 300 Hz to 300 kHz), the coupling capacitor may be decreased by the same proportion (from 10 μF to 0.01 μF).

In general for a given value of R a large coupling capacitor is required for low frequencies and vice versa.

For a range of frequencies the value of the coupling capacitor is determined by the lowest frequency. Considering the above example, a 10 μF capacitor calculated to provide adequate coupling at 300 Hz will provide more than adequate coupling at 300 kHz. On the other hand a 0.1 μF capacitor calculated to provide adequate coupling at 300 kHz does not provide anything like adequate coupling at 300 Hz.

Decoupling

Figure 22.2b shows a capacitor C decoupling a resistor R. Without the capacitor (Fig. 22.2a) point A has a d.c. voltage of

Fig. 22.2 Effect of decoupling capacitor (a) Without decoupling capacitor (b) With decoupling capacitor

10 V and an a.c. signal voltage of 10 mV. The capacitor being open circuit for d.c. does not therefore interfere with the d.c. voltage at point A. However, if the value of C is such that at the operating frequency its reactance is very small compared with R, all the a.c. signal will effectively be short-circuited to earth. Point A will thus have zero signal voltage. The value of C that would provide satisfactory decoupling is determined by resistor R as well as the operating frequency, in the same way as the value of the coupling capacitor described above.

R–C coupled amplifier

Figure 22.3 shows an $R-C$ coupled amplifier where C_1 is the input coupling capacitor. The value of C_1 is comparatively large due to the low input impedance of the CE transistor which is made even smaller by R_2 shunting the input. C_2 couples the output to the load or the next stage and is of a similar value to C_1. Typical values of coupling capacitors are as follows:

for a.f., 10 μF–50 μF;   for r.f., 0.01 μF–0.1 μF.

Fig. 22.3 *R-C* coupled amplifier with decoupling capacitor C_3

Decoupling capacitor

The negative feedback produced by R_4 in Fig. 22.3 on the one hand provides the necessary d.c. stability, while on the other reduces the gain of the amplifier to a very low level of the order of 2 to 3. The reduction in the gain is due to the a.c. negative feedback provided by the signal voltage drop across R_4. In order to remove the a.c. negative feedback while retaining d.c. stability, emitter decoupling capacitor C_3 is used.

Typical values for emitter decoupling capacitors are of the same order as those for the coupling capacitor.

Amplification

The circuit in Fig. 22.3 is the complete circuit for a single stage CE amplifier. When an input signal, e.g. a sine wave, is fed as

Input

Output

Fig. 22.4 Phase reversal

shown C_1 couples the signal to pass through to the base. For the positive half cycle, the base goes away from the emitter, V_{be} goes up, I_e and hence I_c increases, bringing V_c down. Thus the positive half cycle of the input produces a negative-going half cycle at the output. On the other hand the negative half cycle of the input produces an upward or a positive movement in the collector voltage. The output is thus out of phase with the input as shown in Fig. 22.4. Amplification occurs because a very small swing in V_{be} produces a large swing in transistor current which, when passing through R_3, produces a large voltage swing at the collector.

The load line

Transistor output characteristics show the general operation of the transistor. In order to represent the operation of the transistor when used in a circuit, a load line is drawn. Figure 22.5 shows the output characteristics for the transistor used in Fig. 22.3 with XY as the load line.

Before the load line can be drawn, two points falling on it have to be located. The most convenient points are point X on the x-axis where $I_c = 0$ and point Y on the y-axis where $V_c = 0$. These two points are then joined together to form the load line. Assume $V_C = V_{CE}$.

Point X. At this point, transistor current I_c is zero. The transistor is at cut-off. Hence the collector voltage $V_c = V_{cc}$.

Point Y. Here collector voltage $V_c = 0$. Putting $V_c = 0$ in the

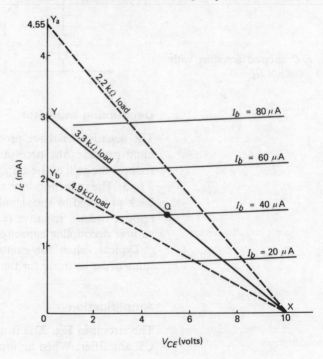

Fig. 22.5 The load line

equation $V_{cc} = V_c + V_{R_3}$, we get $V_{cc} = V_{R_3}$. But $V_{R_3} = I_c \times R_3$, therefore $V_{cc} = I_c \times R_3$, hence

$$I_c = V_{cc}/R_3$$

Using the values given in Fig. 22.3, points X and Y can be located as follows:

Point X. $I_c = 0$, $V_c = V_{cc} = 10$ V.
Point Y. $V_c = 0$, $I_c = V_{cc}/R_3 = 10/3.3 = 3$ mA

XY is therefore the load line for a load resistor R_3 of 3.3 kΩ.

Using a smaller load resistor, 2.2 kΩ, the load line is shifted to XY_a. Point X is the same as for the previous case since V_{cc} remains at 10 V. Point Y_a however, is at $I_c = V_{cc}/R_3 = 10$ V/2.2 kΩ = 4.55 mA.

On the other hand a higher load resistor, e.g. 4.9 kΩ, would produce a load line XY_b with point Y_b at $I_c = 10$ V/4.9 kΩ = 2 mA.

Graphical analysis

Amplification of a signal takes place along the load line and may be represented as shown in Fig. 22.6. Point Q is the quiescent point representing the no-signal or d.c. operating point of the

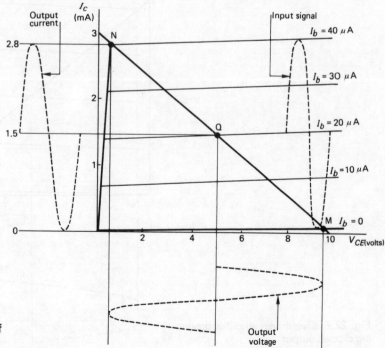

Fig. 22.6 Graphical representation of amplifier operation

amplifier. At the Q-point the transistor is biased to have a base current

$$I_b = 20 \text{ μA with } I_c = 1.5 \text{ mA and } V_c = 5 \text{ V.}$$

When a signal is applied, the base current swings as shown between 0 μA and 40 μA. This produces a collector output current I_c swing of 2.8 mA and a voltage swing of approximately 9 V.

The input swing is restricted on the one hand by the line $I_b = 0$ when the transistor is at cut-off (point M on the load line) and on the other by line $I_b = 40$ μA when the transistor is saturated (point N on the load line). In the case of the amplifier under consideration the Q-point is chosen in the middle so that by feeding a signal of a peak value of 20 μA into the base, the base current swings between zero and 40 μA producing the maximum undistorted output swing shown. Any attempt to enlarge the input signal will result in a distorted output waveform as shown in Fig. 22.7, which is the case of an overdriven amplifier producing clipped sine waves. The input and output waveforms may be represented graphically using the transfer characteristics of Fig. 22.8. The operation is restricted to the linear part, otherwise distortion occurs.

Fig. 22.7 Overdriven amplifier producing clipped output

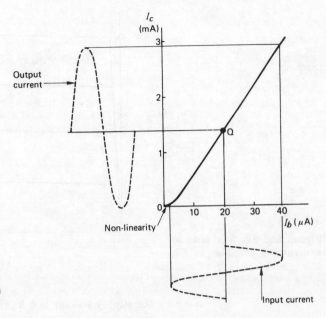

Fig. 22.8 Graphical representation using the transfer characteristics

Transformer coupled amplifier

Interstage coupling can be achieved by means of a transformer as shown in Fig. 22.9. R_1 and R_2 form a bias chain for TR_2 (the bias

Fig. 22.9 Transformer coupled amplifier

chain for TR_1 is not shown). C_2 is the bias decoupling capacitor which prevents any signal from developing across bias resistor R_2. R_3 is the emitter resistor and C_2 is the emitter decoupling capacitor. The primary windings of the two transformers L_1 and L_3 act as the load for TR_1 and TR_2 respectively. Since transformer windings have a very small resistance, the d.c. voltage at the collector is at a constant value of V_{cc}. The signal develops across the winding due to its a.c. resistance, i.e. its reactance. Two load lines can thus be drawn as shown in Fig. 22.10. If

Fig. 22.10 a.c. and d.c. load lines for transformer coupled amplifier in Fig. 22.9

the supply voltage is 6 V, then the d.c. load line is a vertical line representing a constant voltage at the collector of 6 V. The a.c. line represents the operation of the amplifier as the signal is applied. The point of intersection is the quiescent point Q.

Comparison between R–C and transformer coupled amplifiers

$R-C$ coupling is used extensively in electronics due to its high gain, better frequency response, cheap and small-size components. Transformers, on the other hand, are large in size and more expensive. Transformer coupling has two main advantages:

1. It does not use a collector resistance, with the result that power dissipation, i.e. loss in the form of heat, is small compared with the $R-C$ coupled amplifier. Transformer coupled amplifiers are, therefore, more efficient.
2. It facilitates matching between stages (see Chapter 8). If r_1 is the output impedance of TR_1 and r_2 the input impedance of TR_2 (Fig. 22.11), then as was explained in Chapter 8

$$\frac{r_1}{r_2} = n^2 \text{ where } n \text{ is the turns ratio } \frac{T_1}{T_2}$$

Power dissipation

Transistors like other components have a specific power rating which must not be exceeded otherwise the transistor might be damaged.

The power dissipated in a transistor is $I_c \times V_{CE}$ watts.

Fig. 22.11 Transformer matching = $r_1/r_2 = T_1^2/T_2^2 = n^2$

Fig. 22.12 Power dissipation in a transistor = $I_c \times V_{CE}$

For example, referring to Fig. 22.12 with $V_c = 9$ V, $V_e = 1.5$ V.

$$V_{CE} = V_c - V_e = 9 - 1.5 = 7.5 \text{ V}$$

$$I_c = I_e = \frac{V_e}{R_2} = \frac{1.5 \text{ V}}{1.2 \text{ k}\Omega} = 1.25 \text{ mA}$$

Therefore power dissipation in the transistor is

$$I_c \times V_{CE} = 1.25 \text{ mA} \times 7.5 \text{ V} = 9.4 \text{ mW}$$

Note that power dissipated in load resistor R_1 is

$$I_c^2 \times R_1 = (1.25 \text{ mA})^2 \times 4.9 \text{ k}\Omega = 7.7 \text{ mW}$$

The power rating of a transistor may be represented on the output characteristic curve by a hyperbola, i.e. a constant power dissipation curve as shown in Fig. 22.13. Points on this curve represent equal power dissipation. The transistor must, therefore, operate on or below its maximum rated power dissipation curve. To ensure maximum power output, the Q-point is usually chosen to fall on the dissipation curve.

As can be seen from Fig. 22.13, the operation of the transistor is restricted by the saturation line, the cut-off line ($I_b = 0$) and the rated power dissipation curve. The area of operation is shown shaded.

Fig. 22.13 Operating area of a transistor (shown shaded)

23 The common base and common collector amplifiers

Fig. 23.1 CB amplifier with E_1 and E_2 providing the bias voltages

The CB amplifier

Figure 23.1 shows an amplifier using a transistor in the common base configuration. Two separate batteries are used to provide the necessary bias. C_1 is a coupling capacitor feeding the input between the emitter and the base. The output is taken across the load resistor R_4.

Figure 23.2 shows a practical i.f. amplifier using one d.c. supply. The load is a tuned circuit C_3-L_1 employing transformer coupling, C_1 is the input coupling capacitor, R_1-R_2 forms the bias chain, and R_3 is the emitter resistor. C_2 is a decoupling capacitor ensuring that the base is at zero a.c. potential. In this case, the decoupling capacitor is taken to the supply line instead of the chassis. This is permissible since the supply line is at zero potential as far as a.c., i.e. the signal, is concerned. The difference between the supply line and the chassis is a d.c. potential only.

Fig. 23.2 Typical i.f. amplifier employing CB configuration

The CB amplifier has a low input impedance ($50-100\ \Omega$) and a low gain compared with the CE configuration. It has the advantage, however, of a good high frequency response. Hence it is used at very high frequencies, e.g. r.f. amplifiers in radio and TV receivers, i.f. amplifiers for f.m. receivers, etc.

Phase relationship

If the input signal is negative-going, the emitter goes away from the base, and I_c increases to produce a drop in the collector or output voltage. The output is, therefore, in phase with the input.

The CC amplifier

Figure 23.3(a) shows a circuit using a transistor in the common collector configuration. C_1 and C_2 are the input and output coupling capacitors and R_1-R_2 forms the bias chain for the base voltage.

Fig. 23.3 The emitter follower (or common collector) amplifier. (b) shows the normal way in which the circuit is drawn

No collector resistor is used since the output is taken at the emitter. Figure 23.3(b) shows the way the circuit is drawn normally. The output develops across the emitter resistor R_3 and hence the circuit is known as an *emitter follower*. It has a high current gain with a voltage gain of just below one. The low voltage gain is due to the 100% negative feedback produced by R_3.

Phase relationship

When the input signal is positive-going, the base goes away from the emitter, i.e. V_b increases producing an increase in emitter or output voltage. Hence the output is in phase with the input.

Comparison between CE, CB and CC configurations

Config- uration	Input impedance	Output impedance	Phase reversal	Advantages
CE	1–2 kΩ	10–50 kΩ	Yes	High voltage and power gain
CB	Very low	Very high	No	Good high frequency response
CC	Very high	Very low	No	(a) Low output impedance (b) High current gain

24 Photoelectric devices

Types of photoelectric devices

The **photo-emissive cell** or phototube, which employs the principle of electron emission from a cathode when light falls upon its surface.

The **photoconductive cell**, which reduces its resistance as the intensity of light falling upon it is increased.

The **photovoltaic cell**, which generates an e.m.f. according to the intensity of light falling upon its surface. Semiconductor material such as selenium may be used; it produces a high enough voltage to deflect a voltmeter and can be used in lightmeters. The photovoltaic cells are also used to provide power for telephone repeaters and for communication satellites. They form the basis of solar generators where sunlight is used to generate electric power.

Photodiodes and **phototransistors**. In the photodiode a pn junction is reverse biased. The only current passing through the junction is, therefore, a small leakage current, which is a nuisance when the junction is used normally. In the photodiode it becomes the working current. It was found that the leakage current not only increases with heat but also with light waves falling upon the junction. That is why diodes and transistors are packed inside opaque containers. Photodiodes on the other hand are provided with a small window through which light can fall on the junction increasing its leakage current.

Phototransistors use the same principle as the photodiode. The junction in this case is the reverse biased base−collector junction. The advantage of the phototransistor is that the increased b−c leakage current due to light is amplified by the transistor which may then provide enough power to deflect a voltmeter as in the case of a lightmeter. Figure 24.1 shows a simple phototransistor circuit. Multiple phototransistors may be used to drive a motor.

The light emitting diode

In a forward biased pn junction, electrons travelling from the

Fig. 24.1 Circuit using a photo-transistor

$-V_{cc}(-22 \text{ V})$

R_1 (180 kΩ)

R_3 (22 kΩ)

R_2 (10 kΩ)

R_4 (1.8 kΩ)

C_1

TR_1

Fig. 24.2

Fig. 24.3

n-region are injected into the p-region. Some of these electrons combine with the holes in the p-region. These combinations result in a release of energy in the form of visible light. For a large and efficient energy release, materials such as gallium-arsenide are used instead of silicon or germanium as the semiconductor material. Such semiconductor devices are known as light emitting diodes (LED) (Fig. 24.2). The wavelength of the light emitted, i.e. its colour, depends on the material used. Red and green emission are the most popular colours normally used.

Opto-couplers or isolators

An important use of light emitting diodes and photo-sensitive devices such as the photodiode or the phototransistor is in opto-coupling. In its simplest form, an opto-coupler or isolator consists of an LED emitting infra-red light which is picked up by a photo-sensitive device. Both the LED and the photo-sensitive device are enclosed in a single package (Fig. 24.3). Opto-coupling is superior to transformer coupling in switching and chopping applications. It has greater immunity to noise, hum, transients and bounce. Signal transfer is unidirectional with the result that changes in the load conditions have no effect on the input. Opto-coupling is also faster than isolation transformers or relays.

25 Field effect transistors

The field effect transistor (fet) is a semiconductor device that is becoming very popular in modern electronic equipments. It consists basically of a semiconductor current-carrying channel, the resistance of which is controlled by an electric field, thereby controlling the flow of current through the channel.

Field effect transistors are known as **unipolar** transistors since the flow of current is carried out by the majority carriers only. It flows through one type of semiconductor, either an n-type or a p-type. The action of the normal junction transistor on the other hand is based on minority as well as majority carriers. This is because its current flows through a forward biased b−e junction (majority carriers) and a reverse biased b−c junction (minority carriers). Hence they are known as **bipolar** transistors.

Field effect transistors have three electrodes known as the source (s), the gate (g), and the drain (d). They correspond to the emitter, base and collector for the bipolar transistor.

Field effect transistors require no heating and are small in size. They have very high input impedance. They are less temperature-sensitive than the bipolar transistors and hence less prone to thermal runaway. Circuits using fets are simple in design, using fewer components than an equivalent circuit using bipolar transistors.

Field effect transistors are simple to manufacture, and more amenable for use in integrated circuits than their counterparts, the bipolar transistors.

There are two main types: the junction field effect transistor and the MOS field effect transistor.

The junction fet

Consider an n-type semiconductor channel with a d.c. potential V_{DD} connected across it as shown in Fig. 25.1a. A current known as drain current I_D flows through the channel from source to drain as shown. If now a p-type region known as the gate is diffused into the n-type channel as shown in Fig. 25.1b, a pn junction is formed. At the junction a depletion layer is established in

Fig. 25.1 The operation of a junction fet

Fig. 25.2 Cross-section of the structure of a junction fet

Fig. 25.3 Junction fet symbols

the same manner as a normal pn junction. As can be seen, the depletion layer restricts the flow of current through the channel by reducing the effective width of the channel. In other words it increases the resistance of the channel. The depletion layer may be widened, thus restricting further the flow of current by applying a reverse bias V_{GS} to the junction as shown in Fig. 25.1c. By changing the bias voltage at the gate, drain current I_D may be varied. Figure 25.2 shows a cross-section of the structure of a field effect transistor.

FETs with p-type channel may also be used, with negative d.c. supply $-V_{DD}$. The symbols for both types of junction fets are shown in Fig. 25.3.

Output characteristics

The output characteristics for a junction fet used in the common source configuration is shown in Fig. 25.4. They are similar to the output characteristics of a bipolar transistor. They show how output current I_D changes with output voltage (voltage between drain and source) V_{DS} for specific values of gate bias (voltage between gate and source) V_{GS}.

The change in gate–source bias is large (in the region of a few volts) unlike the bipolar transistor where the base–emitter voltage is basically constant.

It can be seen that as the gate bias increases, so drain current decreases, until the depletion layer due to the gate–channel junction fills up the whole width of the channel, stopping the flow of current. The fet is then said to be cut off.

Pinch-off voltage

Consider the output curve with $V_{GS} = 0$ (Fig. 25.4). As the drain voltage V_{DS} is increased from zero, drain current increases gradu-

Fig. 25.4 The output characteristics of a junction fet

ally until point P, after which it stays constant. The voltage at point P is known as the pinch-off voltage. At this point the depletion layer due to the reverse biased gate–channel junction has extended right across the channel. Drain current I_D does not stop flowing, however, because the depletion layer is created precisely because of the drain current itself. For grid bias of -1 V, -2 V, and so on, similar pinch-off points are observed P_1, P_2, etc. Joining these points together forms the pinch-off region where the fet is made to operate.

The fet common source amplifier

A typical a.f. amplifier using a field effect transistor is shown in Fig. 25.5. R_1 is a leakage resistor which provides a path for the leakage current to go to chassis; R_3 provides the necessary reverse bias by giving the source a positive voltage above that of the gate. R_3 also provides d.c. stability for the amplifier. R_2 is the load resistor which may be as high as 1.5 MΩ. C_2 is the source decoupling capacitor removing the a.c. negative feedback caused

Fig. 25.5 a.f. amplifier using an n-channel junction fet

by R_3. It will be noticed that a low value coupling capacitor of 0.1 µF is used. This provides adequate coupling due to the high input impedance of the fet.

When a signal is applied into the input, the fet drain current will vary accordingly, producing an output voltage at the drain. For the positive half cycle, the gate goes in the positive direction, thereby reducing the reverse bias of the gate–source junction, and thus increasing the fet current I_D. As I_D increases, drain output voltage decreases and a negative-going half cycle is produced. On the other hand, the negative half cycle of the input produces a positive-going half cycle at the output. Hence the output is in anti-phase to the input.

Calculations

One advantage of the field effect transistor is its very low leakage current which is in the region of a few pico-amperes (10^{-12} mA). Hence the gate is at zero potential. Current through the fet flows from drain to source and it is usually referred to as drain current I_D (= source current I_S).

Consider the circuit in Fig. 25.5. Given a drain current I_D = 0.2 mA then source voltage V_S = 0.2 mA × 5 kΩ = 1 V, giving a reverse bias at the gate of 1 V.

Voltage across R_2 = 0.2 mA × 30 kΩ = 6 V.

Therefore drain voltage V_D = 15 − 6 = 9 V.

The load line

A load line may be drawn in the same way as that for a bipolar transistor. Figure 25.6 shows the load line for the amplifier in Fig. 25.5.

When I_D = 0, V_{DS} = V_{DD} = 15 V giving us point X on the load line.

When V_{DS} = 0, the total d.c. supply V_{DD} falls across R_2.

$$\text{Hence } I_D = \frac{V_{DD}}{R_2} = \frac{15 \text{ V}}{30 \text{ k}\Omega} = 0.5 \text{ mA giving us point Y.}$$

The quiescent point Q is chosen so that the transistor operates within its pinch-off region.

Quiescent or operating point Q is hence at I_D = 0.2 mA and V_{GS} = −1 V with V_{DS} = 9 V.

MOSFET

This type of field effect transistor has a metal gate which is electrically insulated from the semiconductor, by a thin oxide film. Hence its name MOS, which stands for Metal Oxide Silicon.

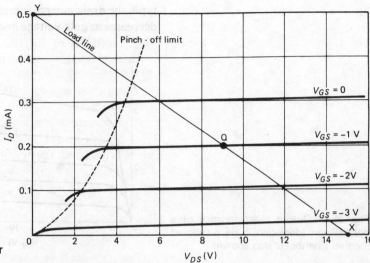

Fig. 25.6 Load line for the fet amplifier in Fig. 25.5

Fig. 25.7 Cross-section of a mosfet

The n-type channel is formed by the gate insulating oxide attracting electrons from a p-type substrate (Fig. 25.7). The thickness of the n-channel may be varied by applying a voltage to the gate. A positive voltage widens the n-type channel, increasing the current, while a negative voltage narrows the n-channel and reduces the current. The opposite is true for a p-channel type.

There are two types of mosfets: the enhancement (normally off) and the depletion (normally on). In the **enhancement** type the fet is at cut-off (normally off), when gate bias $V_{GS} = 0$. Current flows only when a bias voltage is applied to the gate. The output characteristics for an n-channel enhancement type are shown in Fig. 25.8, together with its symbol.

Fig. 25.8 The output characteristics of a normally-off (enhancement) type n-channel mosfet. (Symbol is also shown)

The **depletion** type conducts (normally on) without a gate bias. The gate voltage may be positive or negative. For an n-channel type, the drain current increases as gate voltage goes positive and decreases as gate voltage goes negative (Fig. 25.9).

Fig. 25.9 Output characteristics of a normally-on (depletion) type n-channel mosfet. (Symbol is also shown)

Normally - on (Depletion)

The symbols for p-channel mosfets are shown in Fig. 25.10. Note that the broken lines indicate a normally off (i.e. enhancement) type. A continuous line, on the other hand, indicates a normally on (depletion) type. Contact b is the substrate lead which is normally taken to source potential. Figure 25.11 shows a typical amplifier using a p-channel depletion mosfet in the common source configuration. A negative d.c. supply is used. The positive bias between the gate and source V_{GS} is produced in the normal way by source resistor R_3.

Normally - off (Enhancement)   Normally - on (Depletion)

Fig. 25.10 Symbol of p-channel mosfet

Fig. 25.11 Fet amplifier using a p-channel depletion type

26 More solid state devices

The tunnel diode

The tunnel diode is a pn junction using heavily doped semi-conductors and a very narrow depletion layer. Because of the heavy doping, the tunnel diode conducts in the reverse as well as in the forward direction. Hence it is only used when forward biased.

Fig. 26.1 Symbol and forward characteristics of a tunnel diode

Figure 26.1 shows the forward characteristics for a tunnel diode. As the forward bias is increased from zero, the diode current increases sharply up to a maximum at point p. Further increase in the voltage causes the current to decrease to a minimum value (point M) after which the current begins to rise again. For the region between P and M the diode current decreases while its voltage increases. This is opposite to a normal resistor where its current increases as its voltage increases. Hence this region is known as a **negative resistance** region. Devices such as the tunnel diode having negative resistance characteristics are capable of setting up oscillations without the aid of feedback. This is made use of in high frequency oscillators and switching purposes.

The zener diode

The zener diode is a junction diode which has a specified reverse breakdown voltage. Unlike the ordinary diode the zener is operated at its breakdown voltage. Figure 26.2 shows the characteristics for a zener diode. In the forward direction it behaves in the same way as a normal diode. When reverse biased, little current flows until the zener reaches its breakdown voltage V_Z, usually known as the zener voltage, when current suddenly begins to flow. At breakdown the voltage across the zener remains constant for a very large change of current. Zener diodes are used for shunt stabilisation and for voltage reference (see Chapter 28).

Fig. 26.2 Forward and reverse characteristics of a zener diode

The switching diode

The switching diode consists of four layers of semiconductor material as shown in Fig. 26.3. When the diode is forward biased a very small current flows until breakdown occurs (Fig. 26.4). Before breakdown the diode may be considered as a switch in the 'off' position. After breakdown it may be considered as a switch in the 'on' position.

Fig. 26.3 Switching diode

The controlled rectifier

The controlled rectifier or the **thyristor** is another 4-layer pnpn junction device usually made of silicon; hence the more common

Fig. 26.4 Characteristics of a switching diode

Fig. 26.5 The SCR, its symbol and various outlines

Fig. 26.6 Characteristics of the SCR

name, the silicon controlled rectifier (SCR). Unlike the switching diode the SCR has a third terminal known as the gate (Fig. 26.5). The critical breakdown voltage may now be varied by the potential at the gate. Figure 26.6 shows the characteristics of an SCR for two different values of gate current. At zero gate current (i.e. a gate potential of zero volts), the SCR has a breakdown voltage of V_1. If the gate is given a positive voltage with respect to the cathode to drive a gate current I_{g1}, the SCR breaks down at a lower voltage V_2. Once the SCR starts to conduct, the gate potential has no effect on the current through it. The SCR may be switched off only by making the anode voltage fall below the cathode potential.

The SCR is widely used because of its fast switching and because a very small gate current (i.e. a very small power) is sufficient to trigger the SCR even though it may be handling a current of several amperes.

It is extensively used for power rectification. It turns on during the positive (or negative) half cycle only, thus producing pulsating d.c. Power control is achieved by switching on the SCR for longer or shorter periods of time (see Chapter 28).

Figure 26.7 shows an SCR triggered by a train of pulses. The SCR switches on at the positive edge of the pulse and stays on until the input falls to zero, producing an output which is part of the positive half cycle of the input as shown.

Fig. 26.7   Pulse triggered SCR

Figure 26.8 shows a.c. triggering using a variable resistor VR_1 to control the SCR. The SCR is triggered by the input waveform itself. When VR_1 is set to its minimum value, triggering occurs early as shown in Fig. 26.8a. As VR_1 is increased, the triggering is delayed since the amplitude of the waveform going into the gate gets smaller. At the maximum value of VR_1 the SCR is triggered just before the positive peak as shown in Fig. 26.8b. Note that the SCR in the circuit under consideration may only be triggered during the first quarter of the cycle, i.e. before the positive peak arrives at the gate. If it fails to do that, it will not trigger at all and the output would be zero.

To achieve triggering during the second quarter of the cycle, i.e. after the positive peak has passed, a phase shift network is used as shown in Fig. 26.9. Capacitor C and resistor VR_1 act as the phase shift network. The waveform fed into the gate suffers a delay (or a phase shift) as shown in Fig. 26.9b. As stated above,

Fig. 26.8 The SCR rectifier

Fig. 26.9 SCR rectifier employing a phase shift network VR_1-C

the SCR may only be triggered before the positive peak arrives at the gate. But due to the phase shift, by the time the positive peak arrives at the gate, the positive peak of the input has already passed. Hence the SCR may now be triggered during the second quarter of the input cycle, as shown in Fig. 26.9c.

The varactor

It is found that a reverse biased pn junction diode has a small capacitance across it which varies with its reverse voltage. This fact is used in the fabrication of integrated circuits in order to include capacitors within the silicon slice.

Reverse biased diodes are used as variable-capacitor diodes known as vari-cap diodes or varactors (Fig. 26.10). Varactors are employed in, among other things, automatic frequency control systems and programmable instruments. What is commonly known as electronic tuning also employs varactors as the tuning capacitors.

Fig. 26.10 Variable capacitor diode or varactor

Compared with the common variable capacitor, the varactor is smaller in size, more sensitive, and has very high stability and reliability.

The unijunction transistor

Another device which has a negative resistance is the unijunction. Figure 26.11 shows the symbol and characteristics of a p-type unijunction. As soon as the emitter voltage is high enough to forward bias the pn junction between the emitter and base b_1, current begins to flow from the emitter with the voltage across the junction falling to a low value (about 0.6 V). Unijunctions are often used as oscillators (see p. 201) and for triggering purposes.

Fig. 26.11 Unijunction. (a) p-type symbol (b) characteristics

Fig. 26.12 The diac. (a) symbol (b) outline

The diac

The diac is another switching device, with two terminals T_1 and T_2, as shown in Fig. 26.12. By increasing the potential between T_1 and T_2, regardless of polarity, breakdown occurs. The diac may conduct in either direction and hence it is also known as a bidirectional diode. When breakdown occurs, the voltage across the diac falls to few volts as shown in Fig. 26.13. Breakdown voltages are in the region of 30–50 V. The diac is used as a triggering element, e.g. for SCRs.

The triac

The triac (Fig. 26.14) is another bidirectional diode with a controlling gate terminal. Breakdown occurs when the voltage between the two terminals T_1 and T_2 reaches a specified level, regardless of the polarity.

The triac can be triggered into conduction by a gate signal which may be either positive or negative with respect to T_1 or T_2. Triacs are also used as triggering devices, e.g. for SCRs.

Fig. 26.13 Diac characteristic

Fig. 26.14 The triac. (a) symbol
(b) outlines

Integrated circuits

Advances in technology have resulted in improvements in
reliability of electronic devices as well as a reduction in cost and
size. Microelectronic circuits are simply a miniature assembly of
a number of electronic components, both passive and active.

There are two types of micro-circuits: the film circuits and the
monolithic integrated circuits. There are two types of film-
integrated circuits, known as thick film and thin film. Both are
constructed by depositing films of special resistive paste on an
insulating surface. Mainly used for resistors, they may also be
used for small-value capacitors and inductors.

The monolithic integrated circuit normally referred to as the
integrated circuit (IC) uses a basic *p*-type silicon disc or chip. The
silicon chip is a very thin wafer (0.02 cm thick) with a surface
area (approximately 26 mm²) equivalent to the cross-sectional

area of a match stick. The chip acts as a substrate into which various components are fabricated by a process known as diffusion. Integrated circuits may contain a number of active devices, transistors, diodes, etc., as well as resistors and capacitors. *Large scale integration* (LSI) can produce ICs containing complete systems, e.g. decoders and microprocessors.

Although integrated circuits are solid devices and physically strong, electrically they are delicate and must be handled with care. The following precautions must be taken when replacing ICs:

1. ICs should be handled by their casing, avoiding touching the pins, otherwise dirt and grease may accumulate, reducing contact.
2. When soldering an IC, extreme care must be taken to ensure that it does not get too hot. Overheating will readily damage most ICs.
3. The correct specified d.c. voltages must be used. Most ICs need highly regulated d.c. supplies. This is especially important in digital applications.
4. Power dissipation of most ICs with the exception of power amplifiers is very small. Overloading must therefore be avoided as this may cause the IC to exceed its rated dissipation, causing overheating and damage.
5. When making measurements on an IC, care must be taken not to short-circuit adjacent pins. Specially shaped or pointed probes should be used.
6. When not in use, ICs (MOS type) have their pins shorted together. This should be done whether the IC is kept on the shelf or is being packaged for transportation.

27 R–C filters, clippers and clampers

A filter allows one frequency band to pass through without attenuation (weakening) and cuts off all other frequencies. The frequency at which cut-off occurs is known as the cut-off frequency f_c (Fig. 27.1).

 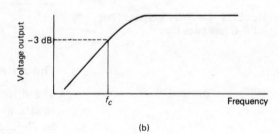

Fig. 27.1 Frequency response (a) Low pass filter (b) High-pass filter

Effect on a square wave

As explained in Chapter 3, a square wave is a complex waveform consisting of a fundamental and an infinite number of odd harmonics. A square wave can thus be thought of as consisting of a low frequency component represented by the flat top and bottom, and a high frequency component represented by the fast rising and falling edges.

When fed through a filter, the square wave suffers a distortion in its shape. In general, a low pass filter will distort the high frequency edges, rendering them less sharp and producing rounded corners as shown in Fig. 27.7(b). (A low pass filter has the same effect on a square wave as an amplifier with insufficient bandwidth.) Conversely, a high pass filter distorts the flat top and bottom of a square wave as shown in Fig. 27.5(b).

Fig. 27.2

R–C filters

The simplest type of a filter is an $R-C$ filter. It uses the fact that the reactance of a capacitor varies inversely with frequency, while a resistance remains constant as frequency changes. Figure 27.2 shows a capacitor in series with a resistance. At low input frequencies, the reactance of the capacitor is very large compared with resistance R. Hence the voltage v_c across the capacitor is large while that across the resistor v_r is low. At high input frequencies the opposite is true, namely v_c is low and v_r is high. Therefore if an output is taken across the capacitor (Fig. 27.3a), low frequencies will predominate while high frequencies will be greatly attenuated. In other words we have a low pass filter. Conversely, an output across the resistor produces a high-pass filter (Fig. 27.3b). The values of R and C determine the cut-off frequency.

Fig. 27.3 (a) R-C high-pass filter
(b) R-C low pass filter

The differentiator

The differentiator is a high-pass filter which when fed with a square wave produces high frequency spikes. Figure 27.4 shows an $R-C$ differentiator. Capacitor C allows the high frequency component of the input through (Fig. 27.5). The capacitor then begins to charge up to 10 V.

Fig. 27.4 R-C differentiator

Provided the time constant (the product of C and R) is short compared with the periodic time of the input waveform, the capacitor will become fully charged to 10 V well before the next high frequency component CD arrives (Fig. 27.5a). When the capacitor is fully charged, the voltage across the resistor, i.e. the output, is zero. The falling edge CD represents a 10 V drop and, being a high frequency component, will pass through the capacitor bringing the output voltage down to -10 V. The capacitor then begins to charge up to -10 V, and given the short time constant

Fig. 27.5 Output from the differentiator in Fig. 27.4 (a) Short time constant (b) Long time constant

Fig. 27.6 *R-C* integrator

Fig. 27.7 Output from integrator in Fig. 27.6 (a) Long time constant (b) Short time constant

the capacitor will be fully charged, with the output falling to zero well before the next high frequency edge arrives and so on. The effect of a time constant that is long compared with the period of the input is shown in Fig. 27.5b.

The integrator

The integrator is a low pass filter which when fed with a square wave produces a triangular waveform. Figure 27.6 shows an $R-C$ integrator. At the first rising edge of the input (Fig. 27.7), the capacitor begins to charge up towards $+10$ V. Provided the time constant CR is long compared with the period of input, the falling edge CD arrives well before the capacitor is fully charged (Fig. 27.7a). The falling edge CD will attempt to charge the capacitor in the negative direction. Again, due to the long time constant, before the capacitor can charge up negatively, the next edge EF arrives, and so on. The output waveform will, therefore, be triangular in shape having a low amplitude compared with the input.

The effect of a short time constant is shown in Fig. 27.7b. Note that for both a differentiator and an integrator, the time constant is always compared with the period of the input. A time constant of 100 μs for example is long compared with a periodic time of say 5 μs (input frequency of 200 kHz) but short compared with a periodic time of say 5 ms (an input frequency of 200 Hz).

The effect on a sine wave

A sine wave is a pure waveform with no harmonics. When fed into a filter of any type it suffers no change in its shape. Its amplitude may be affected, depending on whether the frequency of the sine wave falls within the passband of the filter or outside it. In the former case, the sine wave suffers very little attenuation, while in the latter it may be very largely attenuated.

The effect on a saw-tooth waveform

The effect of integration on a saw-tooth waveform is to round off the sharp edges, as shown in Fig. 27.8. How far the sharp edges are removed is determined by the degree of integration, i.e. the time constant of the circuit. A very long time constant (a high

Fig. 27.8 Effect of integration on a saw-tooth waveform

Fig. 27.9 Effects of differentiation on a saw-tooth waveform

degree of integration) will produce the effect shown in Fig. 27.8(b).

The effect of differentiating a saw-tooth waveform is that shown in Fig. 27.9. A high degree of differentiation, i.e. a very short time constant, will produce the spiky pulse shown in Fig. 27.9(b).

Diode clipping

A **clipper**, also known as a limiter, flattens or slices the top or bottom or both of a waveform. The circuit in Fig. 27.10 clips the whole of the negative half cycle. The forward voltage drop of the diode would produce a 0.6 V negative excursion shown in dotted

Fig. 27.10

line. Usually the forward voltage drop is neglected and diodes are assumed ideal.

To produce clipping at other levels, an e.m.f. may be added in series with the diode to forward bias the diode (Fig. 27.11a) or to reverse bias the diode (Fig. 27.11b). In the circuit in Fig. 27.11b the diode conducts only when its cathode is at or below -2 V, assuming ideal diode. Cathode voltages above -2 V will keep the diode reverse biased, i.e. open circuit, and hence that part of the waveform appears at the output.

Fig. 27.11 (a) Clipping at $+2$ V (b) Clipping at -2 V

A simple method of working out the output of a diode clipper with an external e.m.f. is as follows:

1. Draw a line representing the e.m.f. level along the input waveform.
2. If the e.m.f. is connected in such a way as to forward bias the diode, then the larger part of the waveform will be clipped off and vice versa.

The circuits in Fig. 27.12 produce clipping of both positive and negative half cycles. In Fig. 27.12a, D_1 clips the positive half while D_2 clips the negative half cycle. For ideal diodes the output would be zero. However, due to the forward voltage drop across the diodes (0.6 V for silicon diodes) clipping occurs at $+0.6$ V and -0.6 V.

Figure 27.12b shows a circuit which is in effect a doubling of that shown in Fig. 27.11b. D_1 clips the positive half at $+2$ V while D_2 clips the negative half at -4 V.

Zener clipping

Zener diodes can also be used for clipping a waveform as shown in Fig. 27.13. Z_2 in Fig. 27.13b conducts for the whole positive

Fig. 27.12 Positive and negative clipping

Fig. 27.13 Zener clipping

half cycle. However Z_1 stays off until the input voltage exceeds its breakdown voltage (6 V in this case) clipping the input as shown. During the negative half cycle, Z_1 conducts and Z_2 clips the waveform at -9 V.

Transistor clipping

As explained in Chapter 9, clipping can be achieved by over-loading an amplifier. The circuit in Fig. 27.14 produces an output which is practically a square wave. The transistor has no bias voltage, hence it is at cut-off without an input. During the positive half cycle the transistor switches on (its base going away from the emitter) and provided the input is large enough it saturates, given an output of zero. During the negative half cycle of the input, the transistor remains off and the output is at $+V_{cc}$.

Fig. 27.14 Transistor clipping

The output is a square wave and hence the circuit is known as a squarer.

Schmitt trigger

A very useful circuit for squaring, clipping and pulse shaping is the Schmitt trigger shown in Fig. 27.15. With no input, TR_1 base is at zero potential and the transistor is cut-off. TR_2 however is saturated since its base has a positive voltage determined by potential divider $R_2-R_4-R_5$. The output (TR_2 collector) is practically at zero potential. TR_2 current flowing through the common emitter resistor R_3 gives the emitters a positive voltage which reverse biases TR_1.

Fig. 27.15 Schmitt trigger circuit

When the input is increased in the positive direction, TR_1 begins to conduct when its base reaches TR_1 emitter voltage $+0.6$ V. When that happens, its collector potential drops and with it TR_2 base voltage. This leads to a drop in TR_2 current resulting in a drop in emitter (TR_2 and TR_1) potential causing TR_1 to conduct even more and so on. This results in TR_1 saturating and TR_2 turning off very quickly, with the output going to V_{cc}. If the input voltage is now decreased towards zero the reverse operation will occur resulting in TR_1 OFF, TR_2 ON.

The clamper

Also known as d.c. restorer, the clamper provides a.c. waveforms with a d.c. level. A clamper does not change the shape of the input signal, it just provides it with a d.c. component.

There are many occasions where it is important to retain the d.c. level of a signal. The d.c. level is sometimes lost due to a.c. coupling and has to be restored, e.g. a pulse train following differentiation or a video signal following a coupling capacitor. Clamping is also used to provide Class C biasing for transistors when used in oscillators for example (see Chapter 29). Figure 27.16 shows a clamper circuit.

Fig. 27.16 Clamping. (a) Circuit producing zero clamping (b) Output (point X) changing from zero to 10 V as the input changes from -5 V to $+5$ V

Falling edge AB (Fig. 27.17) of the input represents a drop of 10 V which, being of high frequency, will pass through the capacitor making point X (the output) go negative. The diode is forward biased and assuming it to be ideal, it will act as a short circuit across the output clamping point X to zero. The capacitor quickly charges up through the small diode forward resistance in the negative direction as shown in Fig. 27.16b. This charge is retained till the next rising edge arrives.

Rising edge CD represents a 10 V positive step which, being of high frequency, passes through the capacitor shifting point X from zero volts to $+10$ V (Fig. 27.16b). The diode is now reverse biased (i.e. open circuit) with 10 V across resistor R. Current begins to flow and attempts to charge the capacitor in the opposite direction; the voltage at the output begins to fall. However, if the time constant CR is long compared with the periodic time of the input, the capacitor is unable to lose its

Fig. 27.17 Output of clamper in Fig. 27.16 (a) with time constant very long, (b) with time constant short and (c) with time constant very short

negative charge and the output remains at practically the same potential until the next falling edge arrives (Fig. 27.17a).

For a time constant that is not long compared with the period of the input, the output is as shown in Fig. 27.17b. With a short time constant the circuit becomes a differentiator, having its negative-going spikes fully clipped (Fig. 27.17c).

To ensure a long time constant, resistor R may be removed, making the time constant equal to $C \times r$ where r is the reverse resistance of the diode.

The diode may be reversed to produce zero clamping with negative-going waveform (Fig. 27.18). Note here that the input itself has a d.c. level which is removed by the capacitor and hence does not affect the output.

Fig. 27.18 Zero clamping with negative going output

To draw the output waveform for a given clamping circuit, first redraw the input waveform and if the diode is connected in such a way as to clip positive excursions, the waveform will be negative-going only and vice versa, having exactly the same amplitude as the input.

Clamping circuits can be used to clamp waveforms other than

square waves. Figure 27.19 shows a circuit for sine wave clamping. Clamping at levels other than zero are possible by adding an e.m.f. in series with the diode to give it a forward bias, as in Fig. 27.20a, or a negative bias as in Fig. 27.20b. In Fig. 27.20b the diode is given a reverse bias of 5 V thus preventing the output from going above +5 V. Since a clamping retains the amplitude of the input, the output drops to −15 V resulting in a total amplitude of 20 V.

Fig. 27.19 Clamping of a sine wave

(a)

Fig. 27.20 (a) Clamping at −5 V
(b) Clamping at +5 V

(b)

28 Power supplies II

Rectification

There are two types of rectifier.

1. **Half-wave rectifier**, shown in Fig. 28.1. Diode D_1 in Fig. 28.1a allows only the positive half cycles through, producing a positive-going output. When the diode is reversed as in Fig. 28.1b negative-going half cycles are produced. The output waveform contains a d.c. level which is 0.318 (approximately one-third) of the peak voltage (Fig. 28.2).

Fig. 28.1 Half-wave rectifier (a) Positive-going (b) Negative-going

Fig. 28.2

2. **Full-wave rectifier**, shown in Fig. 28.3. A transformer with a centre tapped secondary is used. Two equal and opposite waveforms are developed across each half of the secondary winding. For one half of the input, point A is positive and point B is negative with respect to the centre tap, and vice versa for the other half cycle. When A is positive, D_1 conducts and current I_1 flows as shown. When B is positive, D_2 conducts and current I_2

157

Fig. 28.3 Full-wave rectifier using a centre tap transformer

Fig. 28.4 d.c. level of a full-wave rectified sine wave is 0.636 of the peak

flows through R_L in the same direction as I_1. The output waveform is therefore as shown in Fig. 28.4 with a d.c. level double that of the half-wave rectifier at 0.636 (approximately two-thirds) of the peak voltage.

The bridge rectifier

Another circuit that produces full-wave rectification is that shown in Fig. 28.5 and known as the bridge rectifier. During the positive half cycle of the input (Fig. 28.6a), point A is positive and point B is negative. D_1 and D_3 conduct and current I_1 flows downwards through load R_L. During the negative half cycle (Fig. 28.6b) point B is positive and point A is negative. D_2 and D_4 conduct and current I_2 flows in the same direction through R_L.

The bridge rectifier does not require a centre tapped transformer. However, a transformer may be used to alter the level of the a.c. input to the rectifier.

Fig. 28.5 Bridge rectifier

Fig. 28.6
(a)   (b)

The reservoir capacitor

In order to reduce the a.c. variation of the rectified waveform, a reservoir capacitor C_1 is used as shown in Fig. 28.7. C_1 charges up to the peak voltage and then discharges through the load R_L, preventing the voltage from falling rapidly. Figure 28.8 shows the effect of the reservoir capacitor on a half-wave and a full-wave rectifier. In both cases the output contains a higher d.c. voltage with a superimposed small a.c. ripple. The amplitude of the ripple is determined by the time constant CR of the reservoir capacitor and the load resistance. Reservoir capacitors therefore have large capacitances of between 100 and 5000 μF.

Fig. 28.7 d.c. power supply with reservoir capacitor C

Fig. 28.8 The effect of the reservoir capacitor on a rectified sine wave

A comparison between the two waveforms in Fig. 28.8 shows that full-wave rectification has the following advantages:

1. The reservoir discharge time is shorter, giving a smaller a.c. ripple.
2. The fundamental frequency of the ripple is twice that of the a.c. supply, whereas for half-wave, the ripple frequency is equal to the supply frequency. For example, using the mains as the a.c. input, the ripple produced by full-wave rectification has a frequency $2 \times 50 = 100$ Hz as compared with 50 Hz for half-wave rectification. Full-wave ripple is easier to filter out due to its higher frequency, as will be seen later.

No-load voltage

The no-load voltage is the terminal voltage of the power unit when load current is zero, i.e. when the load is removed. Figure 28.9 shows a simple power supply with no load resistance. Reservoir capacitor C charges up to the peak voltage as normal. However with the absence of a load resistor, the capacitor retains the charge across it, thus producing a steady output (equal to the peak voltage) without any ripple. The no-load voltage is, therefore, the highest terminal voltage. If the mains supply is used, the no-load terminal voltage

$$V_{nl} = \text{peak voltage} = 1.4 \times \text{r.m.s. voltage}$$
$$= 1.4 \times 240 = 336 \text{ V}$$

a.c. mains

Fig. 28.9 No load voltage = peak input voltage

Peak inverse voltage

An important factor that must be considered in choosing the diodes for d.c. power supplies is the maximum voltage the device has to sustain across it during the non-conducting half cycle known as the peak inverse voltage (PIV). Consider the circuit in Fig. 28.9. The highest potential at the cathode of diode D is the no-load voltage 336 V. The anode potential varies between the positive peak of $+336$ V and a negative peak of -336 V. The maximum peak voltage that the diode has to sustain is when the anode is at the negative peak of -336 V, giving a PIV of $336 + 336 = 672$ V. It can therefore be seen that the PIV is $2 \times$ no-load voltage, i.e. $2 \times$ the peak voltage of the a.c. input.

R–C smoothing

The a.c. ripple may be reduced using a low-pass filter or smoothing circuit. R_1 and C_2 in Fig. 28.10 form a simple $R-C$ filter. To provide adequate ripple attenuation, the time constant $R_1 C_2$ must be very large compared with the periodic time of the ripple waveform. For a given time constant, the shorter the periodic time of the ripple (i.e. the higher its frequency), the more effective is the smoothing. Hence it is easier to smooth out full-wave ripple than half-wave ripple.

Fig. 28.10 d.c. power supply with *R-C* filter

Smoothing capacitor C_2 is large, having a value comparable to that of the reservoir capacitor C_1 of between 100 to 5000 µF. Smoothing resistor R_1 however is given a small value, otherwise a large d.c. drop will develop across it reducing the terminal voltage. Values of smoothing resistors are in the region of 1 to 100 Ω depending on the load current.

L–C smoothing

A more effective smoothing circuit is shown in Fig. 28.11. L_1 and C_2 form a low pass filter. Smoothing choke L_1 has a large inductance (100 mH – 10 H) which tends to smooth out variations in current through it, reducing further the a.c. ripple at the output.

Fig. 28.11 d.c. power supply with *L-C* filter L_1-C_2

Its low resistance is a further advantage while its size is a disadvantage. Note that while the reservoir capacitor C_1 increases the d.c. level of the power unit, the smoothing circuit leaves the d.c. level virtually unchanged. It only attenuates the ripple content.

Regulation

An increase in the current supplied by a power unit causes the terminal voltage to drop. This is due to its internal resistance which is the sum total of the resistance of the transformer winding, diodes, smoothing resistor or choke. Figure 28.12 shows the change in the terminal voltage of a d.c. supply as load current is increased. This curve is known as the regulation curve. The terminal voltage is at a maximum when the load current is zero, i.e. at no load. When it is supplying the specified full load current, the terminal voltage is referred to as the full load voltage.

Fig. 28.12 Regulation curve for an unstabilised power supply

Regulation is given as a percentage and it is defined as

$$\frac{\text{No load voltage} - \text{Full load voltage}}{\text{Full load voltage}} \times 100\%$$

$$= \frac{V_{nl} - V_{fl}}{V_{fl}} \times 100\%$$

For example if a d.c. supply provides 22 V when on no load and 20 V when supplying a full load current of 10 mA, its regulation is

$$\frac{V_{nl} - V_{fl}}{V_{fl}} \times 100\% = \frac{22 - 20}{20} \times 100\% = \frac{2}{20} \times 100\%$$

$$= 10\%$$

Regulated power supplies

The regulation of a power supply can be improved by the use of voltage stabilisation or regulation. The terminal voltage may in this way be maintained at a constant level as the load current is varied. There are two types of regulation: the shunt and the series.

Shunt regulators

Figure 28.13 shows a block diagram for a shunt regulator. Figure 28.14 shows a circuit for a shunt regulated power supply in which the stabiliser element is the zener diode. The zener operates at its breakdown voltage, keeping the voltage across it and hence the

Fig. 28.13 Block diagram for a shunt regulator

Fig. 28.14 A shunt regulated power supply

output voltage constant for a very large variation of current through it.

Shunt regulation is based on a current-sharing principle whereby the sum of the load current I_L and the zener current I_z is kept constant. If the load current is increased by say 2 mA, then the shunt stabiliser current is decreased by the same amount and vice versa.

The series dropper resistor R_1 takes the total current, thus developing a voltage V_1 across it equal to the difference between the unregulated d.c. voltage V_{AB} and the zener breakdown voltage V_z.

$$V_1 = V_{AB} - V_z$$

Using the values given in Fig. 28.13 $V_0 = V_z = 9$ V.

Voltage across R_1, $V_1 = V_{AB} - V_z = 30 - 9 = 21$ V.

Therefore, total current $I_T = \dfrac{21 \text{ V}}{1 \text{ k}\Omega} = 21$ mA

Load current $I_L = \dfrac{\text{Voltage across load}}{\text{Load resistance}} = \dfrac{9 \text{ V}}{1.2 \text{ k}\Omega}$

$= 7.5$ mA

Therefore

Zener current $I_z = I_T - I_L = 21 - 7.5 = 13.5$ mA

If the load current is now reduced to 5 mA, a drop of $7.5 - 5 = 2.5$ mA, the current taken by the zener will increase by 2.5 mA to a new value of $13.5 + 2.5 = 16$ mA.

Under no-load condition when $I_L = 0$, the whole of the total current I_T will now be taken by the zener: $I_T = I_z$. This is one disadvantage of the shunt regulator, namely that regardless of the load, the power supply has to provide a constant maximum current of I_T.

Figure 28.15 shows a typical regulation curve for a shunt stabilised power supply, for the circuit given in Fig. 28.14. The load voltage begins to fall rapidly as the load current increases above the full load current of just under 21 mA. At this value the load current is almost equal to the total current I_T. The fall in the voltage occurs when the zener current is too small for breakdown to occur. For good regulation, the unregulated d.c. voltage is normally chosen to be three times the breakdown voltage of the zener.

Fig. 28.15 Regulation curve for a stabilised power supply

Fig. 28.16 Block diagram for a series stabilised power supply

Series regulation

A better and more efficient stabiliser is the series stabiliser, which employs a transistor or a thyristor as the series element. Figure 28.16 shows a simple block diagram for a series stabiliser. It consists of a series control element with a bleed resistor R to provide a minimum load current.

Series transistor stabiliser

A basic circuit for a series stabiliser employing a transistor is shown in Fig. 28.17. The output is taken at the emitter of TR_1 and, as can be seen from Fig. 28.18 where the same circuit is redrawn, TR_1 is used as an emitter follower. The zener maintains the base of the transistor at a constant potential. The emitter follows the base potential so that it is 0.6 V (for silicon) below the base voltage for a normal forward bias, thus keeping the output voltage constant.

The emitter follower acts as a current amplifier which helps to

Fig. 28.17 A series stabilised power supply

Fig. 28.18 Circuit in Fig. 28.17 redrawn to show the emitter follower configuration of TR_1

supply large load currents for a small input current. The zener acting as a regulator as well as a voltage reference diode takes a smaller current compared with the zener used in the shunt stabiliser. For good regulation the zener current should be approximately 5 times the base current.

The simple series stabiliser considered above suffers from two main disadvantages:

1. For large load currents, power zeners and high gain transistors are required.
2. Limited sensitivity.

The first may be overcome by increasing the current gain by means of an additional transistor TR_2 forming a second emitter follower stage as shown in Fig. 28.19. Load current may be very large (in amps) while zener current remains very small. Sensitivity, i.e. voltage stability, may be improved by amplifying the output voltage before comparing it with the reference zener voltage as shown in Fig. 28.20. TR_1 is the normal series transistor, while TR_2 is the error voltage amplifier. The zener is a reference diode only and hence may have small power rating.

TR_2 compares the output voltage with the reference voltage of the zener. Change in the output voltage is amplified and fed into the base of TR_1 which maintains the output voltage constant. For

(a)

(b)

Fig. 28.19 Series stabilised power supply using two emitter followers (the circuit is redrawn in (b))

Fig. 28.20 Series stabiliser using error amplifier TR$_2$ to improve its sensitivity

example, if due to some external disturbance the output voltage V_o increases, TR$_2$ base goes up away from the emitter which is at the fixed voltage of the zener, current through TR$_2$ increases and its collector voltage decreases. TR$_1$ base potential thus suffers a drop towards the emitter which reduces the current through TR$_1$, making load voltage V_o go down and thereby compensating for the original increase.

Many modifications may be made to the series stabiliser in

order to improve its stability and regulation. Figure 28.21 shows a practical circuit used to produce a stabilised 25 V for a colour TV receiver. TR_1 is the normal series stabiliser. TR_2 is a voltage amplifier with its base voltage adjustable by VR_1 to enable the 25 V output to be set up. C_1 and R_3 provide what is known as electronic smoothing. The 100 Hz ripple on the output is fed through TR_2 back to the base of TR_1 in anti-phase to the ripple present there, thus cancelling it out.

Fig. 28.21 25 V stabilised power supply used in TCE 8000 colour TV chassis (By permission of Thorn Consumer Electronics)

Overload protection circuit

One of the problems encountered by a series stabiliser is the protection of the series transistor. An excessive current through the transistor due to an overload or a short circuit may result in permanent damage. One method of protection is shown in Fig. 28.22. TR_2 is the overload protection transistor. R_1 falling in the return path of load current I_L develops a p.d. across it which provides the transistor with a b–e voltage. Provided the load current

Fig. 28.22 Series stabilised power supply employing overload protection transistor TR_2

is normal, the voltage across R_1 is small, keeping TR_2 off. If the load current is increased above its normal value, the potential across R_1 increases giving a forward bias to the transistor, and TR_2 begins to conduct. When TR_2 conducts, it takes current away from TR_1 thus giving it protection. A trip switch may be incorporated to disconnect the power supply if load current increases above its safe value.

Switched mode power supplies (SMPS)

A more efficient power supply is the switched mode. In this type the series regulating element is a switching element (SCR or transistor) which is turned on and off by a pulse or an a.c. waveform to adjust and regulate the d.c. output. The SCR is a very popular switching regulating device (Fig. 28.23). The SCR is triggered at regular intervals. The timing of the trigger pulse determines and thus regulates the d.c. output. For example, if the d.c. output is high, then the trigger pulse is delayed, as shown in Fig. 28.24b, and vice versa, as shown in Fig. 28.24c, thus compensating for those variations. Switching power supplies are more efficient; they are small in size, have a smaller power wastage in the form of heat dissipation as compared with the linear series regulators considered earlier.

Fig. 28.23 Block diagram for a switching mode power supply

Fig. 28.24 Trigger pulse for the switching mode supply in Fig. 28.23 (a) with d.c. output normal, (b) with d.c. output high, (c) with d.c. output low

29 Amplifiers II

Amplifier classification

The operating conditions of amplifiers may be classified into three categories.

Class A

The transistor amplifiers so far considered have been biased in such a way as to operate on the linear part of their characteristics. The Q-point was chosen in the middle to give a maximum undistorted output. These amplifiers are said to operate under class A conditions. Figure 29.1 shows a transistor transfer characteristic. Point A represents class A biasing. The input signal is small enough to keep the b−e junction forward biased. Hence the transistor conducts for the complete cycle, i.e. for 360°.

Class A amplifiers have the advantage of producing an undistorted output, hence their wide use as pre-amplifiers and drivers, and for i.f. and r.f. stages. However, they suffer from low efficiency (about 30%) due to the fact that the transistor conducts and hence dissipates power regardless of the presence or the absence of a signal input.

Class B

Here the transistor is biased at cut off. Point B in Fig. 29.1 shows class B biasing for a transistor. The transistor conducts for alternate half cycles only (i.e. 180°) as shown in Fig. 29.2. Higher efficiency is possible under class B (between 50 to 60%) since the transistor dissipation is limited only to one half of the input cycle. Class B amplifiers are used in push−pull power stages and often have a small forward bias to reduce distortion.

Class C

The transistor is now biased beyond cut off (point C in Fig. 29.1). The transistor conducts for less than half a cycle (i.e. less than

Fig. 29.1 Points A, B and C on the transfer characteristics representing the operating points for classes A, B and C respectively

Fig. 29.2 Class B amplifier: $R_1 - R_2$ provides a small forward bias V_{be} (0.12 V) to avoid non-linearity

169

180°). The output is therefore in the form of a pulsating waveform as shown in Fig. 29.3. It has very high efficiency of between 65 to 85%. Class C amplifiers are used in oscillators and r.f. power amplifiers.

Fig. 29.3 Class C signal biasing (i) (a) Circuit, (b) Clamping effect of $C_1 - R_1$ and b−e junction

(a)   (b)

Biasing

Class A biasing is provided by a potential divider as explained in previous chapters, giving the b−e junction the necessary forward bias.

Class B amplifiers are biased at cut off, i.e. at a base−emitter voltage of zero. No bias chain is therefore necessary. However, to avoid operating in the non-linear part of the characteristics, the transistor is often given a small forward bias of 0.1 to 0.2 V by potential divider $R_1 - R_2$ shown in Fig. 29.2. The Q-point is now slightly above cut off.

Class C amplifiers are biased beyond cut off. In other words the b−e junction is given a reverse bias. This is achieved by using the input signal to bias the transistor. Hence class C biasing is also known as *signal biasing*. Two methods may be used to achieve class C biasing.

The most effective method is that shown in Fig. 29.3a. Without a signal input the base is at zero potential. As shown in Fig. 29.3b, the b−e junction together with C_1 and R_1 act as a clamper for incoming signals, reproducing the input waveform together with a negative d.c. of approximately peak voltage $- v_p$. The base is therefore given a reverse bias approximately equal to the peak voltage of the input. The amount of the reverse bias (or the degree of Class C biasing) may be reduced by reducing the time constant $C_1 R_1$ (usually by choosing a smaller value of R_1).

A second method is that shown in Fig. 29.4. Here the emitter is given a positive potential by the charge on C_3. With the base at zero potential, a positive emitter provides a reverse bias to the b−e junction. As shown in Fig. 29.4b, for the input signal the

Fig. 29.4 Class C signal biasing (ii) (a) Circuit, (b) Rectifying effect of b−e junction R_3 and C_3

(a)　　　　(b)

b−e junction together with C_3 and R_3 act as a rectifier giving C_3 a positive charge.

Cascade amplifiers

Figure 29.5 shows a 2-stage $R–C$ coupled a.f. transistor amplifier. TR_1 and TR_2 are biased in class A by $R_1–R_2$ and $R_5–R_6$ respectively. The two stages are isolated from each other as far as d.c. is concerned by coupling capacitor C_2.

Fig. 29.5 Two-stage a.f. amplifier connected in cascade

Bandwidth

A typical frequency response curve of an amplifier is shown in Fig. 29.6. It shows that the output or gain of the amplifier remains constant at the mid-frequency range but falls at high and low frequencies.

The drop at the low-frequency end is due to the coupling capacitor C_2 in Fig. 29.5. As the frequency falls, the reactance of the coupling capacitor increases, reducing the amplitude of the

Fig. 29.6 Typical a.f. frequency response

signal fed into TR_2. Decoupling capacitors C_1 and C_3 also reduce the low-frequency response but their effect is very small and may be neglected.

The fall at the high-frequency end is due to what is known as *stray* or *interelectrode capacitors* across the transistor. Stray capacitors exist between the various terminals of the transistor. They have the effect of shunting the input and output thus reducing the gain of the amplifier at high frequencies. Every transistor has what is known as a cut-off frequency at which its current gain is too low for amplification to take place. This is an important restriction on the use of a transistor at high frequencies.

The bandwidth of the amplifier is given by the 3 dB points where the output voltage falls to 70% of its maximum value (or where the output power is half its maximum value).

I.F. amplifiers

The i.f. amplifier is a voltage amplifier using a tuned circuit as the load. It operates at intermediate frequencies such as 470 kHz for a.m. radio, 10.7 MHz for f.m. radio, and 39.5 MHz for a TV receiver.

Figure 29.7 shows a typical i.f. amplifier used in an a.m. radio receiver. $R_1 - R_2$ form a bias chain for TR_1, C_2 is the bias decoupling capacitor, C_4 is the emitter decoupling capacitor, and R_3 the emitter resistor for d.c. stabilisation. $C_1 - L_1$ and $C_3 - L_3$ are resonant circuits tuned to an i.f. of 470 kHz. Transformer coupling is used for both the input and output. The purpose of the tapping on the primary of the output transformer T_2 is to improve the selectivity of the i.f. amplifier. Without a tapped primary the low output resistance r_0 of the common emitter transistor falls across the tuned circuit $C_3 - L_3$ thus damping it and reducing its selectivity. With tapping, the primary winding forms a single winding step-up transformer with turns t_1 as its primary and turns t_2 as the secondary as shown in Fig. 29.8. The resistance shunting the tuned circuit is now the equivalent resistance to r_0 when transferred to the secondary, with a turns ratio $n = t_1/t_2$ of less than one.

Fig. 29.7 I.F. amplifier suitable for use in a.m. radio receivers

Fig. 29.8 The effect of tapping a tuned circuit. L_3 is effectively an auto-transformer

Fig. 29.9 Single-ended a.f. transistor power amplifier

Equivalent resistance $R_0 = r_1/n^2$ (see p. 50) is larger than r_0 reducing the damping effect and improving the selectivity of the tuned circuit.

Power amplifiers

Amplifiers so far considered are what have been referred to as voltage amplifiers, the purpose of which is to produce a large voltage gain. Where output power is required, for instance to feed into a loudspeaker or an r.f. aerial or to drive a motor, power amplifiers must be used. They have high power gain which is achieved by high voltage and current gains.

Class A operation

Figure 29.9 shows a basic single-ended transistor output stage. Class A operation must be used for undistorted output. Efficiency is very low with a large drain from the d.c. supply. It can deliver small power outputs only. It may be used in car radios where current drain is unimportant.

Push–pull operation

Push–pull output stages are almost universally used in modern transistorised amplifiers. Push–pull amplifiers use two transistors operating in Class B, each one amplifying one half cycle of the input.

Push–pull using two similar transistors

Figure 29.10 shows a simplified circuit of a push–pull amplifier.

Fig. 29.10 Push–pull amplifier using two identical transistors with a transformer phase splitter

The b–e junctions are zero biased with each transistor conducting for alternate half cycles only. Input transformer T_1 has a centre tapped secondary which acts as a phase splitter. Two equal and opposite (anti-phase) signals are produced across each half cycle of the secondary winding: v_a in phase with the input and v_b in the anti-phase to the input. While the positive half cycle of v_a represents the positive half cycle of the input, the *positive* half cycle of v_b represents the *negative* half cycle of the input. TR_1 and TR_2 conduct when their bases go positive with respect to their emitters. Thus TR_1 conducts for the positive half cycle of v_a with current i_1 flowing as shown from emitter to collector through the top half of output transformer T_2 towards V_{cc}. This induces a positive half cycle across the secondary of the T_2. TR_2 conducts for the positive half cycle of v_b with its current i_2 flowing upwards (opposite to i_1) through the bottom half of transformer T_2 inducing a negative half cycle at the secondary winding. The centre tapped output transformer therefore combines the two half cycles to produce one complete cycle. TR_1 and TR_2 are connected in the common emitter configuration thus having a relatively high output impedance. Since the load to the output stage is usually very small, e.g. a 10 Ω loudspeaker, a matching transformer T_2 is always used.

The output waveform produced by the zero biased push–pull amplifier suffers from the cross-over distortion shown in Fig. 29.10. This is due to the non-linear part of the characteristics of the two transistors. It takes place during the period when one transistor begins to switch off and the other transistor begins to switch on. To overcome cross-over distortion, the transistors are given a small forward bias of betwen 0.1 and 0.2 V, as shown in Fig. 29.11, where R_1-R_2 provide a bias chain for both transistors. The non-linearity of the two transistors cancel each other out producing an undistorted output.

Fig. 29.11 R_1-R_2 bias chain providing small forward bias to remove cross-over distortion

Transistor phase splitters

Figure 29.12 shows a phase splitter using an npn transistor. R_3 and R_4 have equal value to give two equal and opposite sine waves at the two outputs taken at the emitter and the collector. For maximum undistorted outputs, the ratio of $R_1:R_2$ should be between 2:1 and 3:1. Typical quiescent d.c. voltages are shown on the circuit.

Fig. 29.12 Transistor phase splitter

The complementary push–pull

The complementary push–pull power amplifier avoids the use of either a phase splitter at the input or a transformer at the output. It uses two symmetrical transistors, a pnp and an npn, known as a complementary pair. It uses the fact that a positive-going signal switches an npn transistor on, while a negative-going signal switches a pnp transistor on. Figure 29.13 shows the basic circuit for the complementary push–pull. TR_1 and TR_2 are biased in class B (i.e. at cut off). Two d.c. supplies are used: $+ V_{cc}$ and $- V_{cc}$. The positive half cycle of the input switches TR_1 on and TR_2 off. TR_1 current i_1 flows from $+ V_{cc}$, through load resistor R as shown. For the negative half cycle, TR_2 conducts with its current i_2 flowing towards $- V_{cc}$ from chassis through load R in opposite direction to i_1. A whole sine wave will thus appear across the load, corresponding to both halves of the input cycle. It should be noted that since the output is taken at the emitters of the transistors, TR_1 and TR_2 are therefore common collector or emitter follower amplifiers.

Fig. 29.13 Basic circuit for push–pull complementary amplifier

Figure 29.14 shows a complete circuit for a complementary push–pull power amplifier together with the driver. The circuit is now modified to use one single d.c. supply. TR_1 is the driver amplifier biased in class A by resistor chain R_1–R_2. When the d.c. supply is switched on, TR_1 conducts normally. Coupling capacitor C_3 has no charge across it. Hence point A, the emitters of TR_2 and TR_3, is at zero potential. The bases of TR_1 and TR_2 however are at a positive potential determined by the voltage at the collector of TR_1. This positive voltage switches TR_2 on. TR_3 being a pnp transistor is switched off. TR_2 conducts as shown with its current i_2 charging C_3. As C_3 charges up, the voltage at point A rises. This continues until TR_2 switches off which takes place as soon as its emitter voltage (point A) is the same potential

Fig. 29.14 Complementary push–pull power amplifier using independent biasing chain for driver TR_1

as its base. If TR_1 is designed to have a collector voltage of $\frac{1}{2}V_{cc}$ (4.5 V), then TR_2 switches off as soon as point A is at $\frac{1}{2}V_{cc}$ potential. The circuit remains balanced in this way with a $\frac{1}{2}V_{cc}$ applied across each transistor. TR_2 and TR_3 are biased at cut off (class B) with a b–e junction bias of zero volts.

When an input signal is applied, TR_1 conducts for the whole cycle, amplifying the input and providing the necessary drive for the output transistors TR_2 and TR_3. The complementary pair then amplify the signal as described for the basic circuit above.

The circuit in Fig. 29.14 suffers from d.c. instability. Any change in TR_1 current produces a change in the quiescent condition of the output pair which may result in distortion. To avoid this, negative d.c. feedback is used to bias TR_1 as shown in Fig. 29.15. The d.c. voltage at point A ($\frac{1}{2}V_{cc}$) is fed back to the base of TR_1 via resistor R_F. In this circuit the loudspeaker load is connected to the d.c. supply with C_3 as the coupling capacitor. It should be noted that with this arrangement TR_3 provides the charging current for C_3 while TR_2 current discharges it. In general the transistor 'in series' with the coupling capacitor charges the latter while the transistor 'in parallel' discharges it. R_4 provides the output transistors with a small forward bias to remove cross-over distortion. R_6 and R_7 are the emitter resistors for TR_2 and TR_3 respectively. They provide d.c. stability as well as a small signal negative feedback to improve the bandwidth of the amplifier.

Feedback in amplifiers

Figure 29.16 shows a feedback system where a portion of the output voltage is fed back to the input. Voltage v_f is the fed-back voltage which is added to the overall input voltage v_i to produce the effective input voltage e_i. The feedback network B feeds all or

Fig. 29.15 A typical complementary push–pull power amplifier. TR$_1$ is biased via feedback resistor R$_F$

Fig. 29.16 Feedback in amplifiers

a portion β of the output back to the input. If the output voltage is v_0 then the fed-back voltage is

$$v_f = \beta v_0$$

The overall input to the amplifier is $v_i = e_i + v_f = e_i + \beta v_0$. Hence the gain with feedback is

$$G_f = \frac{v_0}{v_i} + \frac{v_0}{e_i + \beta v_0}$$

For negative feedback, where the fed-back voltage is in anti-phase to the input, the effective input $e_i = v_i - v_f$ giving a low overall gain.

For positive feedback where the fed-back voltage is in phase with the input, the effective input $e_i = v_i + v_f$ giving a high overall gain.

Using the values given in Fig. 29.16 and assuming negative

feedback the following calculations may be made:

Effective input to the amplifier $e_i = 10 - 2 = 8$ mV

Given that the gain of the amplifier without feedback is $G = 100$, then

Output voltage $v_0 = 8 \times 100 = 800$ mV

Hence the overall gain (with feedback) is

$$G_f = \frac{v_0}{v_i} = \frac{800}{10} = 80$$

The percentage feedback β is

$$\beta = \frac{v_f}{v_0} = \frac{2}{800} = \frac{1}{400} = 0.0025 \text{ or } 0.25\%$$

Table 29.1 Comparison between positive and negative feedback

Positive feedback	Negative feedback
(1) High gain	(1) Low gain
(2) Narrow bandwidth	(2) Wide bandwidth
(3) Peaking frequency response	(3) Flat frequency response
(4) Low input impedance	(4) High input impedance
(5) High output impedance	(5) Low output impedance
(6) Introduces instability for both a.c. (hence possible oscillation) and for d.c. (hence unstable quiescent conditions)	(6) Improves stability for both a.c. and d.c.
(7) Used in oscillators	(7) Used frequently to improve stability and widen bandwith

Feedback may also be divided into current and voltage feedback. *Current feedback* is where the fed-back voltage is proportional to the output current, e.g. that due to R_4 in Fig. 29.17. Where the fed-back voltage is proportional to the output voltage, the feedback is known as *voltage feedback*, e.g. that due to $C_2 - R_3$ in Fig. 29.17.

Radio frequency (r.f.) amplifiers

At radio frequencies, e.g. v.h.f. and u.h.f., the effect of the inter-electrode capacitances, especially that between collector and base, becomes very noticeable. To overcome this, the common base configuration is used. However, this configuration presents a low input impedance which loads the preceding stage feeding the amplifier. To rectify this, two methods may be used. The first is

Fig. 29.17 Common emitter transistor amplifier R_4 providing current feedback and C_2-R_3 providing voltage feedback

to use a common emitter amplifier with a neutralising circuit. Such circuits cancel out or neutralise the negative feedback effect of the c−b capacitance by introducing another feedback loop in opposition to it.

The second method is to use a common emitter amplifier in cascode with a common base amplifier (Fig. 29.18). TR_1 is the common emitter amplifier and TR_2 the common base amplifier.

Fig. 29.18 Cascode amplifiers

The input is fed to the base of TR_1 with its emitter decoupled to chassis by C_3. The output of TR_1 collector is fed to the emitter of TR_2 which has its base decoupled to chassis by C_1. The bias for TR_1 and TR_2 is provided by resistor chain $R_1-R_2-R_3$.

Hi-fi

Hi-fi stands for high fidelity, a term applied to sound-producing equipment that gives a realistic re-creation of the original sound

– in other words, high-quality reproduction. Hi-fi systems should therefore have a wide a.f. bandwidth 40 Hz–16 kHz, contain low noise and low distortion.

Tone control

The function of a tone control circuit is to extend or reduce (i.e. reshape) the frequency response curve of the amplifier with a bass control affecting the low-frequency end and a treble control affecting the high-frequency end. Tone control circuits may vary from a simple capacitor in series with a resistor to a very complex arrangement employing feedback. Fig. 29.19 shows a useful tone control circuit with a bass control for the low-frequency end and treble control for the high-frequency end. $VR_1 - C_1$ offers a shunt impedance to the incoming a.f. signal. Since the reactance of C_1 is low at high frequencies, the shunt impedance attenuates high frequencies by an amount determined by the setting of VR_1. $VR_2 - C_2$ offers a series impedance to the signal. C_2 has a high reactance at low frequencies attenuating these frequencies by an amount determined by the setting of VR_2.

Fig. 29.19 Tone control circuit

Loudspeakers

A loudspeaker is a transducer that converts electrical energy into acoustic or sound energy. One of the factors affecting the choice of a loudspeaker is its frequency response, i.e. the range of frequencies it can reproduce. If the frequency range of the loudspeaker is not wide enough, then two speakers, one with good bass response and another with good treble response, may be used. Figure 29.20 shows one possible arrangement using a cross-over network to divide the incoming frequencies range. It consists of a low pass filter $L_1 - C_1$ feeding the bass loudspeaker (known as a woofer) and a high pass filter $L_2 - C_2$ feeding the treble speaker (known as a tweeter).

Other factors affecting the choice of the loudspeaker are output power, efficiency, and impedance for matching purposes.

Fig. 29.20 Cross-over network feeding bass and treble loudspeakers

30 Amplifiers III

D.c. amplifiers

In direct current or d.c. amplification, direct coupling is used as shown in Fig. 30.1. The base voltage of TR_2 is directly coupled to the collector of TR_1. The quiescent (no signal) condition of TR_2 is therefore determined by the previous stage. The absence of coupling capacitors makes d.c. amplifiers useful for low-frequency signals.

Fig. 30.1 Direct coupled (d.c.) amplifiers

D.C. amplifiers suffer from what is known as **drift**, which refers to a shift in the quiescent point of the amplifier caused by changes in temperature. To overcome the effect of drift, thermistors or other temperature sensitive elements may be used as shown in Fig. 30.1.

Another method is to use the emitter coupled configuration, an example of which is shown in Fig. 30.2. The effect of temperature change is greatly reduced since the drift in one stage tends to be cancelled by the other stage, leaving the output free from the effect of drift. The emitter coupled amplifier is used for other purposes such as a differential amplifier.

Differential amplifiers

The differential amplifier has two inputs A and B, and an output which is a measure of the difference of the two inputs. Figure

Fig. 30.2 Emitter coupled pair used as a differential amplifier

30.2 shows a simple differential amplifier circuit using an emitter coupled pair of transistors. The output is taken between the two collectors.

Referring to the circuit in Fig. 30.2, TR_1 and TR_2 are matched transistors and the circuit is symmetrical. Without an input the two transistors conduct equally. The current I_e through the common emitter resistor R_5 is shared equally by TR_1 and TR_2. Hence the voltages at the collectors are equal giving a zero output. A positive input at A increases the current through TR_1, I_e increases, voltage V_e across R_5 increases (TR_2 emitter going towards its base), reducing the current through TR_2. Hence while TR_1 collector voltage goes down, that at TR_2 collector goes up producing an output. A negative input at A produces the opposite effect on the voltages at the two collectors, resulting in an opposite output. Since the circuit is symmetrical, an input at B produces similar results. When an input is fed into both A and B, the output will be a measure of the difference of the two inputs. Although only d.c. inputs have been considered, the circuit functions equally as well for a.c. inputs.

The circuit in Fig. 30.2 rejects signals such as noise and hum that are common to both transistors: this is known as common mode rejection. To improve the rejection ratio, the common emitter resistor R_5 should have as high a value as possible. A transistor is sometimes used in place of the common emitter resistor as shown in Fig. 30.3. Transistor TR_3 has a constant bias provided by $-V_{BB}$ and resistor chain R_1-R_2, thereby producing a constant current I_3. TR_3 thus represents a constant current source and hence a very high resistor.

The operational amplifier

The amplifiers considered so far are built up from separate discrete components, such as transistors, diodes and resistors. With an integrated circuit, all the necessary discrete components

Fig. 30.3 Differential amplifier employing an emitter coupled pair with TR_3 as a constant current device

may be included in a single IC package. One such amplifier is known as the operational amplifier. Originally designed to perform certain mathematical operations, hence the name, the operational amplifier may be employed for a variety of applications.

The operational amplifier is an ideal amplifier with infinite gain, infinite bandwidth and a perfectly flat frequency response, infinite input impedance, zero output impedance, and no drift. In practice, an operational amplifier has the following properties:

Very high gain (over 50 000)
Very wide bandwidth and a flat frequency response
Very high input impedance
Very low output impedance
Very low drift

Figure 30.4 shows the symbol for an operational amplifier. It has two input terminals: an inverting input ($-$) which produces an output in anti-phase to the input, and a non-inverting input ($+$) which produces an output in phase with the input.

Fig. 30.4

Applications

There are a number of applications for an operational amplifier including an inverter, non-inverter, voltage follower, summing amplifier, integrator, differential amplifier and comparator.

External components are connected to the operational amplifier chip to determine its specific application. We will now consider some of these applications.

The inverting amplifier

Fig. 30.5

Figure 30.5 shows an operational amplifier connected as an inverter. With an almost infinite gain, the operational amplifier requires a very small input to produce an output. Point p, the inverting input terminal is, therefore, at **virtual earth**, i.e. almost zero potential. To reduce the gain of the amplifier to the required level, a very large negative feedback is introduced by feedback resistor R_F. It can be shown that the gain of the inverter in Fig. 30.5 is

$$\text{Gain} = -\frac{R_F}{R_1}$$

The negative sign signifies the inverting operation.

EXAMPLE

For an input of 50 mV and given that $R_1 = 1\ \text{k}\Omega$ and $R_F = 2.2\ \text{k}$, calculate the gain and the expected output voltage.

Solution
$$\text{Gain} = -\frac{R_F}{R_1} = -\frac{2.2\ \text{k}\Omega}{1\ \text{k}\Omega} = -2.2$$

$$\begin{aligned}\text{Output} &= \text{Gain} \times \text{Input}\\ &= -2.2 \times 50\ \text{mV}\\ &= -110\ \text{mV}\end{aligned}$$

The summing amplifier

The summing amplifier (Fig. 30.6) provides an output voltage which is proportional to the sum of the input voltages V_1 and V_2. For input V_1, the gain is $-R_F/R_1$. For input V_2, the gain = $-R_F/R_2$.

Fig. 30.6

For example, if $R_F = R_1 = R_2 = 5$ kΩ, then the gain for both inputs $= -5$ k$\Omega/5$ k$\Omega = -1$. Given $V_1 = +1$ V and $V_2 = +2$ V we get an output due to V_1 of $1 \times (-1) = -1$ V and an output due to V_2 of $2 \times (-1) = -2$ V. Hence the total output V_0 is $-1 - 2 = -3$ V.

EXAMPLE 1

Fig. 30.7

In the operational amplifier shown in Fig. 30.7 input $V_1 = 20$ mV and input $V_2 = -10$ mV. Calculate V$_0$.

Solution

The output due to V_1 is $-\dfrac{5}{1} \times 20 = -100$ mV.

The output due to V_2 is $-\dfrac{5}{5} \times (-10) = +10$ mV

Hence the total output $V_0 = -100 + 10 = -90$ mV.

The voltage follower

In this case, the operational amplifier has 100% negative feedback (Fig. 30.8) providing a gain of one. Note that the input and output are in phase.

Fig. 30.8

Fig. 30.9

Offset

For a zero input, an ideal operational amplifier has a zero output. In practice, this is not the case and a non-zero output (voltage and current) is produced even when the input is zero. To overcome this, an offset input current and voltage are introduced of such value and polarity as to produce an output which will cancel the non-zero output.

An offset input current is usually introduced by the addition of a resistor R_2 in the non-inverting input terminal as shown in Fig. 30.9. For optimum conditions

$$R_2 = \frac{R_F R_1}{R_F + R_1}$$

Normally, with a gain greater than 4, R_2 is made equal to R_1. The introduction of R_2 does not change the gain of the inverter,

$$\text{namely } \frac{-R_F}{R_1}$$

The non-inverting amplifier

In this case, the input is fed into the non-inverting terminal as shown in Fig. 30.10.

Fig. 30.10

$$\text{Gain} = \frac{R_1 + R_F}{R_1}$$

$$= 1 + \frac{R_F}{R_1}$$

The integrating amplifier

Figure 30.11 shows an operational amplifier connected as an integrator. The feedback component is, in this case, capacitor C_1. With a step input, the output is a ramp in the opposite polarity to the input, as shown in Fig. 30.12. The rate of change of the output is determined by the time constant C_1R_1 as well as the level of the step input.

Fig. 30.11

Fig. 30.12

$$\text{Rate of change of output} = -\frac{V_1}{C_1R_1} \text{ volts/second}$$

Where V_1 is the input voltage. The negative sign denotes the inverting function.

EXAMPLE 2

(a) Given $C_1 = 1 \ \mu F$, $R_1 = 1 \ k\Omega$ and $V_1 = 3 \ V$, calculate the rate of change of the output, (b) draw a graph of the output.

Solution

Before calculating the rate of change of the output ramp, it is useful to find the time constant of the circuit.

$$\text{Time constant} = C_1R_1 = 1 \times 10^{-6} \times 1 \times 10^3$$
$$= 10^{-3} \ s = 1 \ ms.$$

Rate of change of output

$$= -\frac{V_1}{C_1R_1} = -\frac{3 \ V}{1 \ ms} = -3 \ V/ms$$

Fig. 30.13

This means that the output will change by -3 V every 1 ms. Assuming that C_1 is fully discharged before the input is applied, then after 0.5 ms, the output is -1.5 V; after 1 ms, it is -3 V; after 1.5 ms, it is -4.5 V and so on. It is useful to note that the time constant of the integrating amplifier $C_1 R_1$ is the time it takes the output starting from zero to reach the same value as the input.

To draw a graph of the output ramp, two points are needed. The most appropriate points are A and B in Fig. 30.13. Point A where the output $V_0 = 0$ at time $t = 0$. Point B where output voltage $V_0 = -$ input voltage and time $t = $ time constant $C_1 R_1$. Joining the two points A and B with a straight line gives the graph of the ramp output. In our previous example, A is 0, 0 and B is -3 V, 1 ms.

Fig. 30.14

For the square wave input shown in Fig. 30.14 the output is the waveform shown.

A.C. gain

A sinusoidal input to the integrating amplifier produces a sinusoidal output as well. In this case, the integrator acts as an amplifier with an a.c. gain determined by $C_1 R_1$ as well as the frequency of the input.

$$\text{Gain} = \frac{\text{Capacitor reactance } X_{C_1}}{R_1}$$

$$\text{But } X_{C_1} = \frac{1}{2\pi f C_1}$$

$$\therefore \text{ Gain} = \frac{1}{2\pi f\, C_1 R_1}$$

Fig. 30.15

The difference amplifier

The difference amplifier (Fig. 30.15) provides an output which is proportional to the difference in the input signals $(V_1 - V_2)$. With $R_1 = R_2$,

$$\text{Output } V_0 = \frac{R_F}{R_1}(V_1 - V_2).$$

31 Multivibrators

Multivibrators consist of two transistors arranged so that one transistor is always fully conducting and the other is cut off. Hence a multivibrator has two distinct stable states: TR_1-on/TR_2-off and TR_1-off/TR_2-on. Figure 31.1 shows a basic diagram for a multivibrator circuit where z_1 and z_2 are two coupling elements providing positive feedback.

Fig. 31.1 Basic schematic diagram for a multivibrator

Depending on the feedback element used, multivibrators may be divided into three types.

1. The **bistable** which can stay permanently stable in either state. An external pulse may be used to switch it over from one state to the other. It then remains stable in that second state until triggered by a second pulse and so on.
2. The **monostable** which has one permanent state only. If triggered by an external pulse, it switches over to the other state. It remains in that second state for a duration determined by the time constant of the feedback elements, and returns back to the original state by itself.
3. The **astable** which is a free running oscillator having no permanent state. It continually changes from one state to the other and back again and so on.

191

The bistable circuit

Referring to Fig. 31.2, when the d.c. supply is switched on, because of component tolerances, etc. one transistor will tend to conduct more than the other. However small the difference in transistor currents, it is enough to define the state in which the bistable will settle in.

Fig. 31.2 Bistable multivibrator (a) Circuit using separate d.c. supplies V_{cc} and $-V_{BB}$

Supposing that TR_2 begins to conduct more than TR_1. TR_2 collector voltage will drop causing a drop in TR_1 base voltage, TR_1 current decreases, its collector voltage increases causing TR_2 base to go up away from the emitter. TR_2 current increases further and so on until TR_2 is fully on (saturated) and TR_1 is fully off. In this state TR_1 being at cut off has a collector voltage of $+V_{cc}$ (10 V), while TR_2 being at saturation has a collector voltage of zero volts. The voltage at the base of TR_1 is determined by resistor chain $R_3 - R_5$ and $-V_{BB}$ keeping TR_1 off (Fig. 31.2(b)). The voltage at the base of TR_2 is determined by resistor chain $R_1 - R_6$. As shown in Fig. 31.2(c) TR_2 base has a positive voltage, giving TR_2 the necessary forward bias. The bistable will thus remain in this state permanently if undisturbed by an external pulse. It would remain equally as stable in the other state if TR_1 started conducting more than TR_2 when first switched on.

To avoid using a separate negative d.c. supply, the circuit in Fig. 31.3 is used with R_6 as a common emitter resistor. In either state a voltage V_e develops across R_6 due to the current taken by the 'on' transistor. Thus the two emitters are kept at a constant voltage of V_e. The reverse bias of the 'off' transistor is now achieved by ensuring that its base is at a lower potential than its emitter. Capacitors C_2 and C_3 are known as **speed-up capacitors**. Their purpose is to ensure fast switching from one state to the other.

Fig. 31.3 Bistable multivibrator with steering diodes D_1 and D_2

Steering diodes

To change the state of the bistable, a pulse is fed into it turning the 'on' transistor off. In order to avoid using two separate inputs, steering diodes D_1 and D_2 shown in Fig. 31.3 are employed. The function of these diodes is to steer or guide the trigger pulse to the base of the appropriate transistor. Assuming that the bistable is in the state TR_1-off/TR_2-on, then point X, the common cathodes of D_1 and D_2, has a potential of V_{cc} (10 V). The anode of D_1 is also at V_{cc} (10 V) giving the diode a bias voltage of zero. On the other hand, D_2 anode is at emitter potential (TR_2 being at saturation) of approximately 1 V giving D_2 a reverse bias of -9 V.

If a negative pulse is now applied at point X, D_1 will conduct directing the pulse through R_3 to the base of TR_2 turning it off. As TR_2 turns off, TR_1 switches on and the bistable settles in its alternative state. The bias of the steering diodes is now opposite

Input

One cycle | One cycle

Waveform at point x

$+V_{cc}$ (10 V) —

Output

0.1 V (approx)

One cycle

Fig. 31.4 Input and output waveforms of a bistable multivibrator

to what it was with D_1 having a reverse bias of -9 V. A second pulse will forward bias D_2 directing the pulse through R_4 to the base of TR_1 turning it off and switching the bistable back to its original state.

As the bistable continually switches over, a square wave output may be taken from the collector of either transistor.

Figure 31.4 shows the input and output waveforms of the bistable described above. The square wave input is first differentiated by C_1-R_1. The negative spikes thus produced are used to trigger the bistable, producing the output shown. The positive-going spikes have no effect on the circuit as both diodes will be reverse biased. The output is another square wave having a frequency half that of the input. This is why the bistable is known as a divide by two ($\div 2$) device which is extensively used in counters and calculators.

The monostable

The feedback loop of the monostable (Fig. 31.5) contains one $C-R$ network, C_2-R_2. When the circuit is first switched on TR_2, having its base taken towards V_{cc} via R_2, conducts very heavily, turning TR_1 off in the process. The negative d.c. supply $-V_{BB}$ ensures that TR_1 remains off. This is the stable state of the circuit.

Fig. 31.5 Monostable multivibrator

If a negative pulse is now applied at the input, the high-frequency edge will pass through C_2 to the base of TR_2 turning it off. In a similar way to the bistable, TR_1 will saturate and TR_2 will cut off. The collector of TR_1 (point A) previously at $+10$ V (V_{cc}) goes down sharply to zero volts, a drop of 10 V giving capacitor C_2 a charge of -10 V. In other words TR_2 base (point B) is now at -10 V holding the transistor off. Capacitor C_2

begins to discharge through R_2 from -10 V, attempting to charge up to $+10$ V. The negative potential at point B begins to decrease gradually at a rate determined by time constant C_2R_2. As point B crosses the zero line (Fig. 31.6(b)), TR_2 begins to conduct turning TR_1 off, and the monostable is back to its original state, awaiting the second trigger pulse.

Fig. 31.6 Monostable waveforms

The output of the circuit is a pulse waveform shown in Fig. 31.6c. The pulse width is determined by the period during which TR_2 remains in the off state, itself determined by time constant C_2R_2. The circuit in Fig. 31.5 for example gives a pulse duration of approximately 350 µs. This may be changed by varying the value of C_2 or R_2 or both. It should be noted that while the frequency of the output is the same as that of the input, the pulse width is different. Monostables are used to increase the width of a pulse and for time delay.

The astable

Figure 31.7 shows an astable multivibrator. The feedback loop contains two time constant circuits C_1R_1 and C_2R_2. When the circuit is first switched on, one transistor tends to conduct more than the other. Due to the feedback loop this results in one transistor fully on while the other is fully off. Suppose that TR_1 turns on and TR_2 off with C_1 charging up to $-V_{cc}$ keeping TR_2 off. Capacitor C_1 begins to discharge through R_1 attempting to charge

Fig. 31.7 Astable multivibrator

up to $+V_{cc}$ as in the case of the monostable. As the potential of the junction $R_1 - C_1$ (TR$_2$ base) passes through zero, TR$_2$ switches on, turning TR$_1$ off. C_2 now charges up in the negative direction keeping TR$_1$ off. As C_2 discharges through R_2 it turns TR$_1$ on and so on. The circuit oscillates and produces a square wave output at either collector. The mark-and-space times are determined by the time constants of the circuit.

Figure 31.8 shows the output from the collector of each transistor. For equal mark-and-space, C_1R_1 and C_2R_2 are made equal. Note that as in the case of the monostable, the CR time constant feeding into the base of a transistor determines the time that the transistor remains off.

Fig. 31.8 Outputs from the collector of each transistor of the astable in Fig. 31.7

32 Oscillators

The oscillator is an amplifier with adequate positive feedback to produce an output without an external input. It converts d.c. (the supply to the amplifier) to a.c. signal. Two basic requirements are necessary for sustained oscillations:

(*a*) positive feedback and
(*b*) a gain round the feedback loop of more than one.

There are two types of oscillators: the sinusoidal oscillator producing sine wave outputs; and the non-sinusoidal, also known as relaxation oscillator or multivibrator, normally producing square waves.

Tuned collector oscillators

In Fig. 32.1, $L_2 - C_2$ is the tuned circuit across which the output is developed. Part of the output is fed back to the input via transformer coupling $L_2 - L_1$ in such a way as to be in phase with the input. The transistor is connected in the common emitter mode with $R_1 - R_2$ providing class A biasing. C_1 is a bias decoupling capacitor for R_2. R_3 is the normal d.c. stabilising resistor with C_3 its decoupling capacitor.

Tuned base oscillators

In Fig. 32.2, C_2 is a coupling capacitor which provides class C biasing for TR_1. $L_2 - C_1$ is the tuned circuit. Positive feedback is achieved via C_3 and transformer T_1.

Hartley oscillator

This oscillator (Fig. 32.3) uses a split inductor L_1 to provide the necessary feedback, which is fed into the emitter. $C_2 - L_1$ forms the tuned circuit.

Colpitt's oscillator

A split capacitor $C_1 - C_2$ is used in this case as in Fig. 32.4.

Fig. 32.1 Tuned collector oscillator

Fig. 32.2 Tuned base oscillator

provide an input without an external signal. It converts the d.c. supply to the amplifier into a.c. signal. There are no requirements for an external input signal (no input signal).

All oscillators have in common a *loop gain* greater than one.

The *relaxation oscillator* These oscillators produce non-sinusoidal a.c. waveform, e.g. square, rectangular or triangular. They maintain the square wave signals.

Fig. 32.3 Hartley oscillator   **Fig. 32.4** Colpitt's oscillator

$C_1-C_2-L_1$ forms the tuned circuit, with C_3 providing class C bias.

R–C or phase shift oscillators

Sine wave oscillations may also be produced by using a suitable $R-C$ feedback network as shown in Fig. 32.5. R_1-C_1, R_2-C_2 and R_3-C_3 form a phase shift network which at one given frequency provides 180° phase shift. Since the transistor itself provides 180° phase shift, a total of 360° phase shift is produced round the feedback loop. The feedback is, therefore, positive. Normally R_1-C_1, R_2-C_2 and R_3-C_3 are made equal with each giving a phase shift of 60°. It should be noted that the $R-C$ network provides 180° phase shift at one frequency only, determined by the value of the components.

Fig. 32.5 Phase shift oscillator. R_1-C_1, R_2-C_2; R_3-C_3 provide 180° phase shift

Crystal oscillators

One very important requirement of an oscillator is the stability of its frequency. Changes in frequency may be caused by changes in the values of the tuned circuit components L and C or changes in transistor parameters due to temperature variations. Frequency stability may be improved by the proper choice of the circuit elements including the transistor. For very high stability a quartz crystal is used as shown in Fig. 32.6, with the crystal determining the frequency of oscillation. However, small variations may be achieved by placing a variable capacitor C across the crystal. Crystal oscillators are used in colour TV receivers to produce the 4.43 MHz sub-carrier to an accuracy of a few Hz.

Fig. 32.6 Crystal oscillator. The circuit is used as the reference oscillator in TCE 3000 colour TV receiver Note that the self-capacitance of the inductor is used for tuning. Variable capacitor C is in fact a varactor (By permission of Thorn Consumer Electronics)

U.H.F. oscillators

Oscillators at very high (v.h.f.) and ultra high (u.h.f.) frequencies are similar in operation to other oscillators. However, due to such high frequencies the values of tuning components L and C are very small. The inductor may be a single strip of wire or a simple loop of copper. A varactor may be used for the capacitance. The capacitance and inductance displayed by a short transmission line are sometimes used to produce a tuned circuit.

Non-sinusoidal oscillators

Also known as relaxation oscillators, these produce a square or pulse output by switching one or two transistors on and off. The astable multivibrator is one such oscillator described in the previous section. Another type is the blocking oscillator.

Blocking oscillators

This type uses transformer coupled feedback from collector to base (Fig. 32.7). The action of the circuit hinges around the fact that, due to transformer coupling, a voltage is induced into the base only when collector current is varying, i.e. increasing or decreasing. In the one case the feedback is positive and in the other it is negative. When the circuit is first switched on the transistor conducts and collector current increases thereby producing a feedback voltage at the base in such a way as to switch the transistor further on. When saturation is reached, collector current ceases to increase, inducing a voltage at the base which this time turns the transistor off. The transistor is held in the off state by the negative charge on capacitor C, until the latter is sufficiently discharged through resistor R when the transistor switches on again and so on.

Fig. 32.7 Blocking oscillator

The output from a blocking oscillator is a narrow pulse waveform as shown in Fig. 32.8. The width or mark of the pulse is determined by the transformer parameters while the space is determined by time constant CR. The frequency of oscillation may, therefore, be varied by changing the value of resistor R.

Fig. 32.8 Output of a blocking oscillator

The secondary winding of the transformer acts as the collector load. The rapid change in current through the winding when the transistor switches off causes a large back e.m.f. to be built up resulting in a large overshoot in collector voltage as the transistor switches off. This overshoot voltage may be of such a magnitude as to exceed the maximum rateable collector voltage resulting in damage to the transistor. To protect the transistor a diode D_1 is connected across the primary winding of the transformer as shown. The diode is normally reverse biased. It is forward biased only if the collector voltage exceeds that of the d.c. supply V_{cc}. This way the voltage at the collector cannot exceed that of the supply.

Unijunction oscillators

Devices having negative resistance characteristics such as the unijunction transistor readily lend themselves for use in oscillators. Figure 32.9 shows an oscillator using a unijunction. The unijunction is biased to operate along that part of its output characteristics where the output current increases as the output voltage decreases, i.e. negative resistance. It continually switches on and off without any feedback. The output at base 2 (b_2) is a

Fig. 32.9 Unijunction oscillator

pulse waveform. Another output may be obtained from base 1 (b_1) which is a positive-going pulse waveform. A saw-tooth output may also be taken at the emitter. The periodic time or frequency is determined by time constant C_1R_1.

Saw-tooth generators

Figure 32.10 shows a saw-tooth generator using a pulse input. For the period of the input cycle between A and B (Fig. 32.11) the base of the transistor is at zero voltage and the transistor is cut off. Capacitor C_1 thus steadily charges up through resistor R_1.

Fig. 32.10 Saw-tooth waveform produced from a pulse input

Fig. 32.11 Input and output waveforms of the saw-tooth generator in Fig. 32.10

Before the capacitor is fully charged, positive edge BC arrives, switching TR_1 on and discharging C_1 through the transistor very rapidly. The capacitor remains discharged for the duration of the pulse from C to D. Negative edge DE switches the transistor off and C_1 begins to charge up again and so on.

The same principle of charging and discharging a capacitor is used in other saw-tooth generators. Figure 32.12 shows two such generators using an astable multivibrator and a blocking oscillator respectively. Such oscillators are used in TV receivers for the field timebase. VR_1 controls the frequency (field hold) and VR_2 controls the amplitude (height) of the waveform.

Fig. 32.12 Saw-tooth generators used in the field timebase of TV receivers. (a) Using an astable multivibrator (b) Using a blocking oscillator

33 Logic circuits

Logic circuits are used to perform many functions in electronic equipment such as computers, calculators, process control systems. These circuits are constructed using basic units such as logic gates, registers and counters. Diodes and transistors (bipolar and unipolar) may be used to build up logic circuits.

When employed in gate circuits, diodes and transistors are used as fast switching devices. A diode when reverse (or zero) biased acts as an open circuit similar to an open switch. When forward biased it acts as a short circuit similar to a closed switch. The forward voltage drop (0.6 V for silicon) is small and may be neglected. Switching transistors are used in logic circuits for their fast switching action. When the b−e junction of a bipolar transistor is forward biased the transistor is on (saturated), acting as a short circuit (or a closed switch) with collector potential down to emitter (Fig. 33.1). With reverse or zero bias, the transistor is off, acting as an open circuit with the collector potential at V_{cc}.

Fig. 33.1 The transistor as a switch

Transistor ON   Transistor OFF

Positive and negative logic

In logic there are only two states or levels: 0 and 1. Logic 0 corresponds to zero volts and logic 1 to a specified positive or negative voltage. For positive logic, logic 1 corresponds to a positive voltage (e.g. $+5$ V). For negative logic, logic 1 corresponds to a negative voltage (e.g. -5.2 V). In the rest of this section, positive logic will be assumed unless otherwise stated.

Logic gates may be classified according to the components used. For example, diode–resistor logic uses diodes and resistors, transistor–transistor logic, CMOS logic using FETs and so on.

Diode–resistor logic (DRL)

OR gate

A basic two-input OR gate is shown in Fig. 33.2 and consists of two diodes and a resistor. Positive logic is used with logic $0 = 0$ V and logic $1 = 5$ V. With both inputs at logic 0 level (i.e. both anodes connected to chassis), the diodes are zero biased and current through the resistor is zero giving an output of 0. When input A is at logic 1 level (i.e. D_1 anode connected to a 5 V rail), D_1 is forward biased passing current through R giving an output of 1 (approximately 5 V). When input B is at logic 1, D_2 conducts and output is also 1. Similarly, when both inputs are at logic 1 both diodes conduct and the output remains at 1. The truth table for the gate is shown in Fig. 33.2. Typical input and output waveforms are shown in Fig. 33.3. Note that an output of 1 is present when there is an input at either A or B or both.

A	B	o/p
O	O	O
1	O	1
O	1	1
1	1	1

Fig. 33.2 OR gate. (a) DRL circuit (b) Truth table

Fig. 33.3 Input and output pulses of a 2-input OR gate

AND gate

In the gate shown in Fig. 33.4, the anodes of D_1 and D_2 are connected towards a positive potential (10 V) via load resistor R_1.

A	B	o/p
0	0	0
1	0	0
0	1	0
1	1	1

Fig. 33.4 AND gate. (a) DRL circuit (b) Truth table

Fig. 33.5 Input and output pulses of a 2-input AND gate

When both inputs are at logic 0, D_1 and D_2 are forward biased and act as a short circuit. Hence the anodes will be at the same potential as the cathodes, namely zero. When A is 1 (5 V) and B is 0, D_2 remains forward biased and output remains at 0, giving an output of 0; D_1 however is reverse biased. When both inputs are at 1, 5 V, then both are forward biased and the output at their anodes is at the same level as the input at the cathode, namely 5 V or logic 1. Typical input and output waveforms in Fig. 33.5 show an output of 1 when both inputs are 1.

Resistor–transistor logic (RTL)

NOT gate

A simple transistor inverter may act as a NOT gate as shown in Fig. 33.6. R_1 is a limiter resistor for the base current and R_2 is the

i/p	o/p
1	0
0	1

Fig. 33.6 NOT gate. (a) RTL circuit (b) Truth table

Fig. 33.7 Input and output pulses of a NOT gate

load. With a 0 input, TR₁ is off and the collector is at V_{cc} or logic 1. When the input is at 1, 5 V, TR₁ is ON (saturated) and collector bottomed with output at 0. To ensure that the transistor remains OFF with 0 input, the base is taken to a negative potential $-V_{BB}$ as shown. Typical waveforms are shown in Fig. 33.7.

Note that a NOT gate has one input only. When several inputs are used it becomes a NOR gate.

NOR gate

When both inputs in Fig. 33.8 are at 0, TR₁ is cut off, giving a 1 output. When either or both inputs are 1, TR₁ saturates giving a 0 output. C_1 and C_2 are speed-up capacitors. Typical waveforms are shown in Fig. 33.9.

A	B	o/p
0	0	1
1	0	0
0	1	0
1	1	0

Fig. 33.8 NOR gate. (a) RTL circuit (b) Truth table

Fig. 33.9 Input and output pulses of a 2-input NOR gate

NAND gate

The circuit in Fig. 33.10 employs two transistors in series. When either transistor is off, no current flows through R_3 and output is 1. When and only when both inputs are 1 will TR₁ and TR₂ saturate and output is 0. Typical waveforms are shown in Fig. 33.11.

A	B	C
0	0	1
1	0	1
0	1	1
1	1	0

Fig. 33.10 NAND gate. (a) RTL circuit
(b) Truth table

Fig. 33.11 Input and output pulses of a
2-input NAND gate

NOR gate

Figure 33.12 shows a NOR gate using two pnp transistors
employing negative logic. When both inputs are at 0, both transistors are off and output is 1. When one or both inputs are at
logic 1 level, -5 V, one or both transistors saturates, giving an

Fig. 33.12 NOR gate (RTL circuit)

output of 0. A common emitter resistor R_4 is used to improve the d.c. stability of the gate.

Diode–transistor logic (DTL)

A basic form of a DTL NAND gate is shown in Fig. 33.13. It consists of an AND gate followed by a NOT gate making a NAND gate. One problem that is encountered in DTL gates, such as the one under consideration, is that with one or both inputs at 0, the output from the AND section at point P has a voltage of 0.6 V, the forward voltage drop of D_1 and D_2. Although this voltage still gives logic 0, it is nonetheless enough to forward bias TR_1. To avoid this, D_3 and D_4, called voltage offset diodes, are connected as shown. This way TR_1 will conduct only when potential at P is high enough to forward bias D_3 and D_4 as well as the b–e junction of TR_1, a voltage of approximately 1.8 V.

Fig. 33.13 NAND gate (DTL circuit)

Transistor–transistor logic (TTL)

This type of logic is used in integrated circuits and has the advantage of fast switching action. Figure 33.14 shows a simplified NAND gate using a multiple emitter transistor TR_1 at the input. With both inputs at logic 0, TR_1 saturates, making its collector go down to approximately 0 V. Hence TR_2 is off and the output is 1.

Fig. 33.14 NAND gate (TTL circuit)

Fig. 33.15 NOR gate (fet logic)

Fig. 33.16 NAND gate (fet logic)

With either or both inputs at logic 1, TR_1 turns off, switching TR_2 on to give an output of 0.

FET logic gates

Most logic gates are now manufactured as integrated circuits, ICs. A large number of gates may then be constructed on a tiny chip of silicon of 1 mm × 2 mm. Because of their simplicity, fets are more commonly used than bipolar transistors. One type of this logic is known as CMOS. Figure 33.15 shows a NOR gate similar in principle to that shown in Fig. 33.12 operated by negative logic. VT_1 and VT_2 are p-channel mosfets of the normally-off (enhancement) type. When both inputs are at logic 0 level, VT_1 and VT_2 are cut off giving an output of 1 ($-V_{DD} = -20$ V). When either or both inputs are at logic 1 level (say -20 V) one or both transistors are on, giving an output of 0.

Figure 33.16 shows a NAND gate similar in principle to that in Fig. 33.10 using an n-channel normally-off mosfet. Positive d.c. supply is used and positive logic is necessary to operate the gate. VT_3 is biased permanently on by taking its gate to V_{DD} and acts as a load to the gate. When one or both inputs are at 0 level, one or both transistors are off giving a 1 output. Only when both inputs are 1 will current flow giving an output of 0. Unlike transistor–transistor logic (TTL) where logic 1 = 5 V, in CMOS logic, logic 1 may be anywhere between 3 V and 18 V.

Counters

The basic binary counter is a bistable or ÷2 device also known as a **flip-flop**. A number of these elements constitute a counter. Figure 33.17 shows a binary counter consisting of three flip-flops. Each flip-flop is capable of dividing incoming pulses by a factor of 2. Two successive flip-flops will thus divide by 2 × 2 = 4 (÷4), and three flip-flops divide by 2 × 2 × 2 = 8 (÷8). In other words, for every 8 input pulses, 4 appear at output A, 2 at output B, and 1 at output C, as shown in Fig. 33.17.

Fig. 33.17 3-element binary counter

Table 33.1

repeat

Pulse	Q_A units (2^0)	Q_B twos (2^1)	Q_C fours (2^2)
0	0	0	0
1	1	0	0
2	0	1	0
3	1	1	0
4	0	0	1
5	1	0	1
6	0	1	1
7	1	1	1
8	0	0	0

Table 33.2

repeat

Pulse	Q_A	Q_B	Q_C
0	0	0	0
1	1	0	0
2	0	1	0
3	1	1	0
Feedback	(0)	(0)	(1)
4	0	1	1
5	1	1	1
6	0	0	0

As explained in Chapter 31, only one edge of the input pulse causes the bistable to change its state. The input changes from 0 to 1 and back to 0 and so on for every pulse. It is normally assumed that the negative-going edge of the pulse (i.e. from 1 to 0) changes the state of the flip-flop.

Output Q_A from bistable A represents the 2^0 or units column, output Q_B the 2^1 or twos column, and output Q_C the 2^2 or fours column. Hence after 6 pulses the outputs are as follows: A (units) is 0, B (twos) is 1, and C (fours) is 1, making $0 + 2 + 4 = 6$. In binary coding this is written as 110 in the order CBA. It should be noted that the units column is the first bistable starting from the input. In binary coding on the other hand the units column is always on the right-hand side.

At the seventh pulse all outputs are 1. Pulse number 8 resets all flip-flops back to 0.

Note that the output of each flip-flop represents a column in the binary code. The binary code itself is in the order of CBA.

Feedback

Feedback may be applied to binary counters in order to change the factor by which the input is divided. For example, consider the feedback applied to the 3-element counter shown in Fig. 33.18a. The count proceeds normally up to the third pulse when outputs CBA are 011 (see Table 33.2). The fourth pulse changes A to 0, B to 0, and C to 1. Without feedback, output CBA would be 100. However with feedback the change in C is fed back to B, changing it back to 1, giving CBA reading of 110. Pulse 5 then produces a reading of 111 and the 6th resets all elements back to 0. Thus we have a $\div 6$ counter.

In general it can be shown that a feedback loop reduces the division factor of the bistables inside the loop by 1. Taking the above example, the bistables inside the feedback loop are B and

(a)   (b)

Fig. 33.18 (a) $\div 6$ counter employing feedback across two bistables B and C (b) Reduces the feedback loop to a $\div (4-1)$, i.e. $\div 3$ block

C. Without feedback they divide by a factor of 4. With feedback, bistables B and C form a feedback block having a division factor of $4 - 1 = 3$ as shown in Fig. 33.18b. With bistable A outside the feedback block the total factor of division is $2 \times 3 = 6$.

The decimal counter

Figure 33.19a shows a decimal counter employing two feedback loops. Two feedback blocks are thus formed: block 1 enclosing bistables C and D, dividing by $4 - 1 = 3$; block 2 encloses block 1 together with bistable B. Referring to Fig. 33.19b, without feedback block 2 would divide by $2 \times 3 = 6$. With feedback the division factor is $6 - 1 = 5$. With bistable A outside the feedback loops, the total division factor is thus $2 \times 5 = 10$.

(a)

(b)

Fig. **33.19** (a) Decimal counter (b) Reduction to feedback blocks

Shift register

To transfer data from one part of a system such as a computer to another, two methods are possible. The first and quickest is to transfer all the digits in one operation. Thus, for transferring eight digits, eight separate lines are required. For distances up to a few metres this method is used, but for longer distances such as data transmission between cities this method becomes too expensive. A second but slower method is used. The data information is transmitted digit by digit along a single wire. A shift register may be used to move the binary digits one stage to the left or to the right. The shift register consists of a number of flip-flops capable of rearranging the binary digits in successive order.

Ring counter

A ring counter consists of a standard shift register in which the output is taken back to the input − hence its name. Pulses may thus circulate round the register from the input to the output and back to the input and so on. At the end of each cycle the output may be taken to trigger another counter. For example the output of scale-of-ten or decade counter may be used to trigger another decade counter to make a scale of 100.

Bistables

Bistables were considered in Chapter 31 and a circuit using discrete components was identified. Bistables are very important and useful devices in logic application, and may be made up by the use of logic gates. They are used as a divide by two units, a latch (a single bit memory) or for other applications.

Figure 33.20 shows a $R-S$ bistable, also known as $R-S$ latch. Two outputs are provided Q and $\bar{Q}$ (NOT Q) which are in anti-phase to each other. When $Q = 1$, then $\bar{Q} = 0$ and vice versa. The basic truth table is as that shown in Fig. 33.20. A logic 1 on the reset R input forces Q to 0 (and $\bar{Q}$ to 1) while a logic 1 at the set S input forces Q to 1 (and $\bar{Q}$ to 0).

Truth table

R	S	Q	$\bar{Q}$
0	0	indeterminate	
0	1	0	1
1	0	1	0
1	1	no change	

Fig. 33.20

A development of the simple $R-S$ bistable is the clocked $R-S$ bistable which includes a clock line, as shown in Fig. 33.21. The clock line is essential for synchronous systems, in which case any change-over occurs only when the clock line is at logic 1.

Clk	R	S	Q	$\bar{Q}$
0	X	X	no change	
1	0	1	0	1
1	1	0	1	0
1	1	1	indeterminate	

Fig. 33.21

I.C. packaged gates

Gates are manufactured in integrated circuit form and are provided in packages of a number of identical gates on a single chip. Two main types used are: TTL and CMOS. Examples of such packages are given in Fig. 33.22.

A quad 2-input
NAND gate IC

A hex INVERTER
or NOT gate

A quad 2-input
NOR gate IC

Fig. 33.22

34 Digital display

Fig. 34.1

a a b c d

Fig. 34.2

There are several methods by which the readings of a digital instrument may be displayed ranging from the neon tube to the light emitting diode (LED) and the liquid crystal display (LCD). The number of digits displayed is usually between four and eight. A four-digit display gives a maximum indication of 9999, while an eight-digit display gives a maximum indication of 99999999. For cheaper digital meters, a display known as three-and-a-half-digit display is used. In this type, the most significant digit, MSD (the digit on the extreme left), can only display 0 or 1. Thus the maximum indication is 1999.

The two main types of displays are the light emitting diode (LED) and the liquid crystal display (LCD). Both consist of seven segments, being the minimum number of segments to represent the decimal numbers from zero to nine. The segments are labelled a to g, as shown in Fig. 34.1. Figure 34.2 shows how this type of display may be used to display decimal numbers. The liquid crystal displays require very little power to operate, and are used

Input count	Segments activated	Resulting display 0
0	a b c d e f	0
1	b c	1
2	a b d e g	2
3	a b c d g	3
4	b c f g	4
5	a c d f g	5
6	c d e f g	6
7	d e f g	7
8	a b c d e f g	8
9	a b c f g	9

in portable meters. LED displays require more current than LCD and consume more power. They are widely used in bench DVMs, where power consumption is not a primary consideration. On the other hand, LED displays can be observed in the dark while the liquid crystal display requires ambient light.

LED drive requirement

Figure 34.3 shows a drive system for one 7-segment LED display.

Fig. 34.3

The LED converts electrical current to light. Thus, to illuminate one segment of the display, current must be directed to the diode making up that segment. As shown, one terminal of each diode is connected to a common point. In the example shown, the anodes are connected together making what is known as common-anode configuration. If the cathodes were connected together, the result is a common-cathode configuration.

Each 7-segment display forms one digit of a complete display. Each digit thus has eight terminals, one for each segment and one common connection. In some instances, a decimal point is included in the display, giving a ninth terminal.

Before the segments are driven, the output of the decade

(decimal) counter must be changed into the appropriate signal to drive the display. The output from the counter is in the form of binary coded decimal (BCD) which is a 4-line binary information. It must be converted into an appropriate signal to drive each of the 7 segments. This conversion is carried out by the decoder.

In practice, the switching driver transistors are contained in a single IC package. Furthermore, the functions of the decoder and the driver may be performed by a single IC, e.g. the 7447 for the common-anode and the 7448 for the common-cathode displays. Figure 34.4 shows a 2-digit display unit comprising two decade counters, two decoder/driver packages and two common anode 7-segment displays.

Fig. 34.4

LCD drive requirements

Liquid crystal displays utilise the unique interaction between electrical and optical characteristics of a family of liquids which retain their crystalline form. They give rise to optical properties which make them important for display operations. Since no light is generated (as is the case with LEDs), the display requires very small currents and consumes little power. Because of this, LCDs may be driven directly by MOS and CMOS circuitry.

LCD devices have two terminals or planes; the front plane FP and the back plane BP. The back planes of all segments are connected in common. Alternating voltages are always used for operating liquid crystal displays in order to avoid electrolytic plating and to ensure maximum life.

The method of driving a liquid crystal display involves feeding a low-frequency (typically 40 Hz) square wave to the back plane. (Fig. 34.5). To turn a segment off an in-phase square wave is fed to the front plane and to turn a segment ON an out-of-phase square wave is fed to the front plane. When the driving and control waveforms are out of phase, the resultant waveform across the LCD is twice the amplitude of the driving square wave as shown in Fig. 34.5b which turns the segment ON.

Fig. 34.5

One method of driving an LCD is using an Exclusive-OR gate, as shown in Fig. 34.6. The truth table for an EX-OR gate is as follows:

A	B	C
0	0	0
1	0	1
0	1	1
1	1	0

Fig. 34.6

From the truth table, it can be seen that when the control input A is 0, the output C follows the input in B, i.e. it is in phase with the 40 Hz driving signal at B. This in-phase signal is fed to the front plane of the LCD segment. At the same time, the back plane is directly fed with the 40 Hz driving signal, resulting in zero electric field across the segment. The segment will be OFF. When control input A is logic 1, output C is out-of-phase with input B. This out-of-phase driving signal is fed into the front plane of the LCD segment. With the driving signal fed into the back plane, the resultant electric field across the segment is twice the 40 Hz driving signal. The segment will be ON.

35 Microprocessor applications

Advances made in integrated circuits and the introduction of large scale integration (LSI) have greatly increased the use of microprocessors in computers, control systems, instruments and data logging.

The basic elements of a microprocessor-based system (considered in Chapter 18) are reproduced in Fig. 35.1. The microprocessor, also known as the central processing unit (CPU) carries out the arithmetic and logic operations in accordance with a program stored in memory. The whole system is synchronised and controlled by the CPU.

Fig. 35.1

Memory

There are two main types of memory chips. The Read Only Memory, ROM, is a permanent data store. The data is entered into ROM at the manufacturing stage, and remains there permanently. The CPU can only READ from ROM. It cannot

Binary address				Binary data
0000	0000	0000	0000	DATA
0000	0000	0000	0001	DATA
0000	0000	0000	0010	DATA
0000	0000	0000	0011	DATA
0000	0000	0000	0100	DATA
1100	1110	0110	1100	DATA
1100	1110	0110	1101	DATA
1111	1111	1111	1100	DATA
1111	1111	1111	1101	DATA
1111	1111	1111	1110	DATA
1111	1111	1111	1111	DATA

Fig. 35.2

WRITE into it, i.e. it cannot change the data stored in ROM. The second main type of memory is the Random Access Memory, RAM. Data is stored in RAM temporarily, and may be changed by the CPU. The CPU can thus READ the data stored in RAM as well as WRITE new data into it. Unless a back-up battery is used, the data stored in RAM will be wiped out when the power supply is turned off. This is why such memory is called **volatile**. ROM, on the other hand, retains its data even when the supply is off. Such memory is called **non-volatile**.

The memory chip

The memory chip consists of a number of memory *locations* where data (information) in the form of digital bits may be stored. Each location can normally store an 8-bit binary number. Each location has a unique 16-bit *address*, as shown in Fig. 35.2. The address may be considered as an envelope. The data is the actual information, the letter inside the envelope.

Microcomputer architecture

Figure 35.3 shows the architecture or organisation of a microcomputer system. It shows the manner in which the various elements are connected to each other in a typical microprocessor computer system. The microprocessor CPU is a single chip containing all necessary circuitry to interpret and execute program instructions is terms of data manipulation, logic and arithmetic operations, and timing and control of the system.

Microprocessors are normally mounted as a 40-pin dual-in-line (DIL) package, as shown in Fig. 35.4.

Fig. 35.3

Fig. 35.4

The input/output (I/O) interface

The I/O interface connects the microcomputer to the external devices. It acts as an input or output route for transferring data to and from the microprocessor and external devices such as keyboards, display devices, transducers or drive circuitry for electromechanical devices (stepper motors, relays etc.)

The buses

The main hardware elements in a microcomputer (described above) are interconnected with each other by what is known as a bus structure. A bus is a group of connecting wires or tracks used as paths for digital information that have a common function. There are three main buses in a microprocessor system: the data bus, the address bus and the control bus. The *data bus* is used to transfer data between the microprocessor and the other elements in the system and is normally a bi-directional 8-bit bus.

The *address bus* is used to send the address of memory locations either to retrieve (READ) data from RAM or ROM or to store (WRITE) data into addressed locations in RAM. It is also used to address the input/output interface that may be involved in data transfer. The address bus is uni-directional, carrying 16 bits of digital information simultaneously. The *control bus* is used to send control signals, e.g. clock, read, write etc., from the microprocessor to the other elements of the system. The number of control lines on the bus depends on the microprocessor used and the design of the system.

The clock

A master clock is used in a microcomputer to synchronise the movement of data. This is achieved by using a high-speed crystal-controlled pulse generator. The speed of the clock determines the speed of operation of the microcomputer.

Other applications

Apart from a computer system, microprocessors are widely used in a variety of industrial and domestic applications, from washing machines, cookers, electronic games, weighing machines, automatic testing, process control and data logging. The advantages of using micro-processors in any one application may be one or more of the following:

1. Reduced production costs
2. Improved reliability
3. Reduced maintenance costs
4. Easier operation with reduced human effort.

36 Measuring instruments

Fig. 36.1 The basic meter

Fig. 36.2 Ammeter A connected to measure current I

Fig. 36.3 Voltage measurement

Every meter has certain limitations which have to be taken into account in order to use it in the correct way. The introduction of a measuring instrument into a circuit interferes with its normal condition. The first rule about the use of meters is that this interference must be kept to very small proportions and made negligible. A measuring instrument has a resistance known as the internal resistance which can be represented as shown in Fig. 36.1.

Measurement of current

To measure the current in a circuit, the circuit is opened at a convenient place and an ammeter A is inserted in *series* so that the whole current under test passes through it, as shown in Fig. 36.2. The ammeter could be connected anywhere in the circuit provided that the whole current to be measured goes through the meter.

Good quality ammeters have small internal resistances presenting the minimum interference to the flow of current. Ammeters with large internal resistances give inaccurate readings.

Measurement of voltage

Voltage or potential difference exists across two points in a circuit. To measure voltage, a voltmeter is connected *across* the points, e.g. across a resistor *without* interrupting the circuit. Figure 36.3 shows voltmeter V_1 measuring the voltage across R_1 and voltmeter V_2 measuring the voltage across R_2.

Loading effect

As can be seen from Fig. 36.4 the internal resistance of the voltmeter shunts the circuit resistance R as soon as the voltmeter is connected. Part of the current normally passing through R is diverted through the voltmeter. In other words, resistor R now shunted by the internal resistance of the meter presents a smaller effective resistance to the current I. This is known as the loading

Fig. 36.4 Loading effect I_m is the current diverted into the meter

effect of the voltmeter. To minimise this effect, the internal resistance of the voltmeter is made as large as possible, over 20 times greater than the load resistance. In this way the shunting effect of the meter resistance is reduced to negligible proportions.

Internal resistance

Internal resistance depends on the sensitivity of the meter and the range chosen and can be calculated from the sensitivity, which is quoted in ohms per volt (Ω/V). For example, a voltmeter with a sensitivity of 1000 Ω/V has an internal resistance of

$1000 \times 1 = 1000 \ \Omega$ on the 1 V range
$1000 \times 3 = 3000 \ \Omega$ on the 3 V range
$1000 \times 10 = 10 \ 000 \ \Omega$ on the 10 V range, and so on.

For a given sensitivity, the higher the range chosen the greater the internal resistance and the better the accuracy.

EXAMPLE 1

V_1 and V_2 in Fig. 36.5 are two identical voltmeters having a sensitivity of 20 000 Ω/V. Which meter gives the more accurate reading if both are used on the 10 V range?

Solution

The internal resistance of each meter is 20 000 $\times$ 10 = 200 000 Ω or 200 kΩ.

Meter V_1 shunts R_2 which is a resistance of 10 kΩ. Since the resistance

Fig. 36.5

of the meter is much larger than R_2 (20 times greater), it will give an accurate reading (of 4.5 V). On the other hand, meter V_2 shunts a resistor R_4 of equal resistance, namely 200 kΩ. Thus the loading effect of V_2 is large, giving a misleading reading (of 3 V).

Analogue and digital instruments

Analogue instruments such as moving coil meters and oscilloscopes give a continuous indication of voltage, current, etc. *Digital instruments*, on the other hand, provide a reading in discrete steps. They give a direct reading independent of human error, have no moving parts and are smaller in size and cheaper compared with the analogue type.

Types of measuring instruments

Moving coil

The moving coil meter indicates the average, i.e. d.c., value. It may be used for a.c. measurement by employing a rectifier at the input. Sensitivity is in the region of 20 kΩ/V for d.c. and 600 Ω/V for a.c., with a frequency range of up to 2 kHz or more.

Electronic voltmeter (EVM)

This is basically a moving coil meter with an amplifier at its input. A sensitivity in MΩ/V is produced for both d.c. and a.c. with a frequency range of 3 MHz or more.

Digital voltmeter (DVM)

The DVM has a very high sensitivity (in MΩ/V) with a very wide frequency range (above 2 MHz).

The cathode ray oscilloscope (CRO)

Apart from displaying a waveform, the CRO may be used to measure a variety of electrical quantities including voltage (average and peak), periodic time, phase difference and delay. It has a sensitivity and frequency range similar to the EVM and DVM.

The multimeter

Although we have only considered types of voltmeters, most commercial instruments combine a few functions into one instrument, known as a *multimeter*. This incorporates a switching arrangement enabling the instrument to be used as an ammeter, a voltmeter and an ohmmeter. It may be of the analogue (moving coil) or the digital type.

Logic state testing instruments

The instruments considered above measure an analogue quantity. To test the logic state of a test point, a *logic probe* must be used (Fig. 36.6). When placed at a test point (or node) the logic probe indicates the logic state of the node, '1', '0' or open circuit. The indication is usually given by one or two LEDs. To change the logic state of a node, a *logic pulser* is used. When placed at a node, the pulser changes the logic state of the node to its opposite. If the node is at logic '1' it changes to '0' and vice versa. The pulser is normally used together with a logic probe to test gates, counters, flip-flops and other digital devices.

Indicator lamps Selection switch Power supply cable

TTL CMOS

Probe pin tip H L

Connectors to power supply on board

Fig. 36.6

Another very useful logic testing instrument is the *current tracer*. When placed in the proximity of a printed circuit track, the current tracer can indicate the presence of a pulsating current in the track. No electrical contact is necessary. The tracer is used in conjunction with a logic pulser to identify short circuits between a track or a pin on the one hand, and earth or supply on the other. It may also be used to pinpoint shorts between tracks or pins.

37 Logical fault finding

There are two types of testing procedures that may be used to diagnose a faulty electronic system, device or printed circuit board (PCB): functional and in-circuit testing. Functional testing inspects the unit-under-test to verify its operation, while in-circuit testing inspects each component on the unit-under-test individually to verify its value, polarity etc. Normally, both methods are employed in sequence. With the development of automatic test equipment (ATE), very fast in-circuit testing, where every component on a PCB, including transistors, gates and counters, are tested separately, has become a possibility. Functional testing also acquired new dimensions with the incorporation of computer processing and control. The principles of logical fault finding, however, are the same, whether testing is carried out manually or automatically.

Fault finding must follow a logical sequence, the purpose of which is to identify the cause of the fault and then to rectify it. The number of tests carried out should be kept to a minimum and unnecessary or pointless tests must be avoided. Before any test is carried out, visual inspection of the circuit and the various components should be made to check for burnt-out components, obvious breaks in the printed circuit, and so on. Such inspection should take no more than two or three minutes and with experience will become instinctive. This having been done, without success, proper fault finding procedure can then begin.

First, a **functional test** is carried out where the operation of the board is tested and an attempt is made to identify the faulty block and the suspected faulty component. Before the faulty component is replaced, an **in-circuit measurement** of the component is carried out to confirm the fault.

Functional tests

This type may be divided into two series of tests.

Series I known as **dynamic tests** are applied to the complete electronic equipment in order to isolate the faulty stage or block. Once the fault has been traced to a specific block, then *Series II* or **static tests** are applied to pin-point the cause of the fault to one or two possible faulty components such as a resistor, a capacitor, etc.

Series I tests

These are the first set of tests that are carried out on the faulty electronic equipment. The tests must begin from the output going towards the input. Using the **half-split method** the equipment is initially divided into two appropriate sections. The section at the output is tested first by **injecting** a signal similar to the one normally present at that point. If normal output is produced, the fault must then lie in the remaining section. This section is now divided into two appropriate sub-sections and the same procedure is repeated, and so on until the fault is isolated to the smallest distinguishable stage such as the output stage, i.f. or video amplifier, divider, decoder or a single gate.

EXAMPLE 1: A radio receiver (Fig. 37.1)

Fig. 37.1

The most appropriate division is the a.f. on one hand and the i.f./r.f. on the other. The a.f. section is first tested by injecting a 1 kHz signal at its input (the volume control), via a coupling capacitor (10−50 μF). Low, distorted or no output indicates a faulty a.f. section. The a.f. section is now divided into two sub-sections: the output stage and the pre-amp. Each sub-section is then tested starting from the output. If the fault does not lie in the a.f. section, a pure 1 kHz tone should be heard from the loudspeaker. The fault must then be in the i.f./r.f. section.

A quick check on whether the fault is in the a.f. section or not is the **screw-driver** test. Touch the input of the a.f. section (with the volume control on full) with a screw-driver. A noise from the loudspeaker should be heard if the a.f. section is sound.

If it is found that the fault lies in the i.f./r.f. section a further division is made, namely an r.f. section and an i.f. section. The i.f. section is tested first by injecting an amplitude-modulated 470 kHz signal via a coupling capacitor (0.01−0.1 μF) into the input of the i.f. section, e.g. into the base of the first i.f. transistor. For f.m. receivers a frequency-modulated 10.7 MHz test signal should be used. A sound i.f. section will produce a pure tone (400−600 Hz) at the loudspeaker. Otherwise further sub-divisions are made until the faulty stage is discovered, e.g. one i.f. amplifier or the detector.

If the fault is in the r.f. section, this section is sub-divided if possible and tested as follows. An amplitude-modulated 1000 kHz signal is injected via a coupling capacitor (0.01–0.1 µF) into the input of the stage. The receiver should then be tuned to receive the radio frequency of 1000 kHz or 300 m on the MW. Another appropriate frequency must be used for f.m. receivers.

An alternative to signal injection is the **signal tracing** method where a radio receiver or other electronic equipment is switched on and tuned to a station in the case of a receiver or fed with normal input signal. The presence or otherwise of a signal at appropriate points is confirmed starting from the output. The signal is observed on a cathode ray oscilloscope to test for its waveshape and amplitude.

The above principles for Series I tests can be equally applied to any faulty electronic equipment using appropriate divisions and signal frequencies.

EXAMPLE 2: A digital divider and display (Fig. 37.2)

Fig. 37.2

The first test is applied at a suitable point 'half-way' along the divider chain, as shown. A pulser is used to change the logic state at the input of block 4. The LED at the output should change state if the latch, amplifier and the LED are sound. The fault must then be in one of the dividers preceding block 4. The same procedure is then repeated, using the pulser until one divider is identified as faulty. If the LED does not change state after the first test, then the fault lies in blocks 4, 5 or 6. The same procedure is repeated with the pulser applied to the input of the amplifier and so on.

Principles of Series II tests

Having identified the faulty stage, this series of tests is used to identify the faulty component.

1. Start with d.c. tests. Use a meter having a sensitivity of at least 20 000 Ω/V.
2. Take voltage measurements only. If current value is required, estimate it by measuring the voltage across a known resistor.
3. If the fault is not revealed by d.c. measurements, then, and only then, apply signal tests to the stage.

Fig. 37.3 Normal readings: e 1.1 V, b 1.72 V, c 6.37 V

Fig. 37.4 R_3 o/c, transistor cut off: e 0.3 V, b 0.94 V, c 0.3 V

Table 37.1 Cut-off condition

Fault		Cause
(1) e	zero	
b	zero	
c	V_{cc}	R_1 o/c
V_{be}	zero	
(2) e	high	
b	normal	
c	V_{cc}	R_4 o/c
V_{be}	low	
(3) e	low ($\simeq V_c$)	
b	low	
c	low ($\simeq V_e$)	R_3 o/c
V_{be}	normal	

Application to single stage amplifier (refer to Fig. 37.3)

Usually the normal d.c. readings for the stage are given. If not they could be estimated to a reasonable degree of accuracy. The voltage readings of the faulty stage are then compared with the normal readings. This comparison should then give a good indication of where the fault lies. First determine the static state of the transistor:

(a) transistor at cut-off producing no output signal (or going towards cut-off) or

(b) transistor at saturation producing low distorted output or going towards saturation or

(c) transistor at normal static state.

Once the state of the transistor has been established, the next step is to work out the cause for cut-off or saturation. (When functioning under normal static state, the fault is an a.c. fault which will be dealt with later.)

Cut-off condition

Transistor current ceases to flow, i.e. cut-off, if (a) b–e forward bias is zero or (b) the current path is interrupted, namely when R_3 is open circuit (o/c), when R_4 is o/c, or the transistor itself is faulty. Normally when the transistor is at cut-off, the collector goes up to d.c. supply V_{cc}. However, if R_3 goes o/c the collector is 'floating' and theoretically it is at base potential. As soon as a voltmeter is connected to measure the collector voltage, the base–collector junction becomes forward biased as shown in Fig. 37.4. Current will flow through the meter, the b–c junction and R_1 giving a small reading on the meter. This reading is entirely due to the meter resistance.

Similarly, when cut-off is caused by R_4 going o/c, the emitter is 'floating' and theoretically should be at base potential. However, a voltmeter connected to measure that voltage provides a path for current to flow and forward biases the base–emitter junction, giving a reading on the meter slightly higher than normal (Fig. 37.5).

Table 37.1 gives a summary of the above faults. Note that in the table a high V_{be} refers to an increase of between 0.1 to 0.2 V in the base–emitter forward bias.

Transistor faults also produce cut-off conditions. Voltage readings in such cases depend on the nature of the fault as well as the component values. For example, a b–e s/c (Fig. 37.6) cuts the transistor off and puts R_4 in parallel with R_2 causing base and emitter voltage to go down to a low value determined by the potential divider $R_1–R_2/R_4$. Collector voltage will, of course, be

Fig. 37.5 R_4 o/c, transistor cut off:
e 1.25 V, b 1.74 V, c 10 V

Fig. 37.6 b–e s/c, transistor cut off:
e 0.48 V, b 0.48 V, c 10 V

Fig. 37.7 e–c s/c, transistor cut off:
e 2.29 V, b 1.77 V, c 2.99 V

at V_{cc}. Figure 37.7 shows the effect of a s/c between emitter and collector.

Other transistor faults are given in Table 37.2.

Saturation condition

As explained in Chapter 20, transistor current is determined by the forward bias across the base–emitter junction. A small increase in this bias produces a large rise in transistor current. When the current through the transistor is at maximum value, the transistor is said to be saturated or bottomed. Collector voltage falls as current increases until at saturation it is almost the same as the emitter voltage to within 0.1–0.5 V. In general at saturation, the emitter, base and collector potentials are approximately at the same level. Table 37.3 summarises.

Table 37.2

Fault		Cause
(1) e	zero	
b	normal	
c	V_{cc}	
V_{be}	very high, cannot be sustained by functioning junction	b–e o/c
(2) e	low	
b	low	
c	V_{cc}	b–c o/c
V_{be}	normal	

Table 37.3

Fault		Cause
(1) e	high (V_c)	R_2 o/c
b	high	or
c	low	R_1 low
(2) e	zero	
b	low	C_3 s/c
c	very low	

Normal static state

Normal d.c. voltages with no or low output indicate an a.c. fault, e.g. an open circuit coupling capacitor. Before replacing a suspected o/c capacitor, place a good capacitor of similar value across the suspected component to confirm the fault. An open circuit decoupling capacitor (C_3 in Fig. 37.3) produces low undistorted output. A leaky or short circuit coupling capacitor usually introduces a change in the d.c. state of the transistor depending on the preceding or following stages.

In fault finding the following should be remembered:

1. Do not jump to conclusions by merely comparing one reading with its normal value. The whole set of readings (in the case of a transistor stage the emitter, base and collector) should be noted on paper and compared with the normal set of readings.
2. If accurate readings (up to 0.01 V are possible on a 20 000 Ω/V meter) are taken, then in the vast majority of cases two equal readings indicate a s/c. However, this is not always true and further checks must be made before the final decision is made.

Application to digital gates

In digital applications, the most common faults are what are known as stuck-at faults, namely stuck-at-one (IC pin or node permanently at logic 1) and stuck-at-zero (IC pin or node permanently at logic 0). Other faults may occur including open circuit pins or short circuit between tracks.

Fault diagnosis on logic gates takes the form of stimulating the inputs using a logic pulser and observing the effect on the output using a logic probe. For a full test of the gate, the whole truth table is gone through to verify its operation. For example, consider the digital circuit shown in Fig. 37.8. First the logic states of the input and output of each gate are noted and checked against their respective truth tables. If a gate is then suspected, then a further test on the gate is carried out using a logic pulser and probe. Consider gate G_1. Input pin 2 is permanently at logic 0. To test

Truth table G_2

pin 2	pin 3	pin 1
0	0	1
0	1	0
1	0	0
1	1	0

Fig. 37.8

the gate, a pulser is placed at input pin 3 and a logic probe is placed at output pin 1. By referring to the truth table for NOR gate, it can be seen that with one input (pin 2) at logic 0, a change in the output is produced if the other input (pin 3) is made to change its logic state. For instance, if pin 3 was originally at logic 0, then output pin 1 will be at logic 1. If the pulser is then used to change the state of pin 3 to logic 1, then provided that the gate is sound, a change will be observed by the probe at output pin 1 from logic 1 to logic 0. An opposite change will be observed if pin 3 was originally at logic 1. Similar tests may be applied to the other gates. In each case, attention must be paid to the truth table of the particular gate to ensure that the application of the pulser to one of its inputs does, in fact, produce a change in the output, otherwise the test will be inconclusive.

Fault finding examples

In each example separate fault conditions are described. The fault in each case is assumed to be the result of a failure in a single component, but there may be more than one component that could cause the fault. All test potentials are measured in volts with respect to the chassis, using a 20 000 Ω/V voltmeter.

1.   D.C. coupled amplifier

(Refer to Fig. 37.9)

Test point	1	2	3	4
Normal readings	0.7	0.1	5.1	4.5
Fault A (no output)	0	0	8.65	8
Fault B (no output)	0.01	0.01	8.4	7.75
Fault C (no output)	0.48	0	0.02	0
Fault D (no output)	0.7	0.1	5.1	4.7

FAULT A

TR_1 is cut off, emitter is zero, and collector is at V_{cc}. Cut-off caused by TR_1 base (test point 1) having zero volts. Since the two transistors are d.c. coupled, TR_2 base voltage increases with collector of TR_1, causing TR_2 to saturate.

Answer: R_1 o/c

FAULT B

TR_1 is cut off. Voltages at test points 1 and 2 are equal suggesting a short circuit. This voltage is determined by resistor chain R_1 (1.6 MΩ) in series

$V_{cc} = 9$ V

R_1
1.6 MΩ

R_3
39 kΩ

③

TR₂

①

④

Input

TR₁

② Output

R_2
70 kΩ

R_4
1 kΩ

R_5
4.8 kΩ

Fig. 37.9

with R_2 (70 kΩ) with the latter shunted by R_4 (1 kΩ). As in Fault A, TR₂ is saturated.

Answer: TR₁ b–e s/c.

FAULT C

TR₁ and TR₂ are both cut off. TR₂ emitter voltage is at zero (test point 4) indicating cut off. TR₁ has low collector voltage suggesting saturation, while its emitter (test point 2) is zero. Hence TR₁ must be at cut off caused by the collector resistor going open circuit. TR₁ base is down because of a large base current flowing through high resistor R_1 (1.6 MΩ).

Answer: R_3 o/c.

FAULT D

TR₁ is normal. A saturated TR₂ would produce a high emitter voltage. Since the emitter is almost normal and with the absence of any possible a.c. fault, TR₂ must be at cut off. A faulty transistor, e.g. b–c o/c, would produce zero emitter voltage. An open circuit b–e junction would produce low emitter voltage. The fault must be R_5 o/c with emitter reading (test point 5) due to meter resistance.

Answer: R_5 o/c.

2.   Two-stage R–C coupled fet amplifier

(Refer to Fig. 37.10)

Test point	1	2	3	4	5	6
Normal readings	15	2.4	5.55	0	3.3	12.75
Fault A (no output)	15	0	0	0	3.3	12.75
Fault B (no output)	15	2.4	5.55	5.55	7.5	9.9
Fault C (no output)	15	2.4	5.55	0	4.1	15
Fault D (no output)	15	2.4	5.55	0	6.1	10.8
Fault E (low output)	15	2.4	5.55	0	3.3	12.75

Fig. 37.10

FAULT A

VT_1 cut off. VT_2 normal. Zero drain and source voltages suggests R_2 o/c. Note that if R_3 were o/c, a high source reading would have been obtained.

Answer: R_2 o/c.

FAULT B

VT_1 normal. VT_2 saturated (source high, drain low). A fet may saturate if the gate−source reverse bias V_{GS} is reduced. With an n-channel fet used in the circuit, this may be produced either by the gate voltage going positive (towards the source) reducing V_{GS} or by removing the gate leakage resistor (also see Fault D). Test points 3 and 4 are equal suggesting C_2 short circuit. This will increase VT_2 gate voltage which reduces the reverse bias and increases the current through the transistor.

Answer: C_2 s/c.

FAULT C

VT_1 normal. VT_2 drain at 15 V suggests cut-off. The increase in source voltage (test point 5) points to R_6 o/c with the voltage reading at the source due to meter resistance. Note that a faulty fet such as an open circuit junction would produce cut-off but would give a zero source reading.

Answer: R_6o/c.

FAULT D

VT_1 is normal. VT_2 is saturated (high source, low drain). Since gate voltage remains at zero, saturation is due to gate leakage resistor going open circuit, thus removing the gate–source reverse bias and increasing the drain current.

Answer: R_4 o/c.

FAULT E

All d.c. voltages are normal. Hence fault is a.c. Low output suggests an open circuit decoupling capacitor introducing negative feedback and reducing the gain of the amplifier.

Answer: C_3 or C_5 o/c.

3. Stabilised power supply

(Refer to Fig. 37.11)

Fig. 37.11

Test point	1	2	3	4	5
Normal readings	18	14.1	8.75	9.35	13.3
Fault A	19.5	2.65	0	0.7	2.0
Fault B	19.8	13.5	8.75	9.35	13.5
Fault C	20	20	8.65	0	19.3
Fault D	19.5	0	0	0	0
Fault E	20	20	0	0	0

Note Always start by noting the zener reference voltage. A low or zero reading indicates that the zener is not at breakdown either because of a faulty zener or a fault in the resistor feeding it (R_5 in Fig. 37.11).

FAULT A

Zener reference voltage is zero, which points to a short circuit between test point 3 and chassis. Note that an open circuit R_5 would not give zero reading at test point 3 since the meter resistance would complete the emitter circuit of TR_2 giving a voltage reading.

Answer: Z_1 or C_3 s/c.

FAULT B

Zener voltage is normal. Test points 2 and 5 are the same potential suggesting a short circuit. TR_1 is cut-off, hence its collector (test point 1) has increased.

Answer: TR_1 b−e s/c.

FAULT C

Zener voltage is 0.1 V lower than normal indicating that, while the zener is at breakdown, it is taking a smaller current than normal. This is due to TR_2 being at cut-off (note its collector at 20 V). The cut-off is due to zero volts at TR_2 base indicating a break in the bias chain.

Answer: R_3 or upper part of RV_1 o/c.

FAULT D

The zero volts at the zener is caused by the zero volts at test point 5. TR_2 is at cut-off (base and emitter are both zero volts). Test point 1 is almost normal yet TR_2 collector is at zero volts. This indicates a fault in components R_2 or C_2.

Answer: R_2 o/c or C_2 s/c. (C_2 s/c would anyway cause R_2 to go o/c due to the large current through it.)

FAULT E

Zero zener voltage is caused by zero voltage at test point 5. Voltage across b−e junction of TR_1 = test point 2 − test point 5 = 20 − 0 = 20 V. A pn junction cannot sustain a forward bias higher than 0.7 V.

Answer: TR_1 b−e o/c.

4. Output stage

(Refer to Fig. 37.12)

Test point	1	2	3	4	5
Normal readings	0.61	6.3	6.7	6.45	12
Fault A (no output)	0	12	12	12	12
Fault B (no output)	0.19	0	0.79	1.09	12
Fault C (very low output)	0.4	1.1	1.08	1.08	12
Fault D (no output)	0.61	5.85	6.22	6.0	12

Note Start by looking at test point 4 where the normal reading should be approximately $\frac{1}{2}V_{cc}$. If test point 4 is high, then TR_3 is conducting more than TR_2 and vice versa.

Fig. 37.12

FAULT A

Test point 4 is at V_{cc}. TR_3 is saturated and TR_2 is cut off. TR_1 collector (test point 2) is at V_{cc} indicating TR_1 cut off. TR_1 base is zero volts, hence fault is in bias chain.

Answer: R_2 o/c.

FAULT B

Test point 2 is zero volts suggesting a short circuit to chassis. Such a short circuit would cause TR_2 b–e junction to conduct heavily, charging C_2 and reducing the potential at test point 4. Low TR_1 base voltage is due to low voltage at test point 4.

Answer: TR_2 b–c s/c or C_1 s/c.

FAULT C

Test point 4 is low. C_2 is charged by TR_2 which is conducting more than normal due to its low base voltage (test point 2). The low potential at test point 2 is not due to a saturated TR_1. Note its low b−e forward bias V_{be} of 0.4 V instead of the normal 0.61 V. TR_1 must thus be at cut-off caused by open circuit collector resistance. TR_1 is not fully cut-off. It conducts through the b−e junction of TR_2 thus charging C_2 and bringing test point 4 down to 1.08 V.

TR_3 base is at the same potential as TR_1 collector since no current flows through R_5. TR_3 is at cut-off.

Answer: R_6 o/c.

FAULT D

Readings are approximately normal. Hence the fault is a.c. An open circuit C_2 would produce a voltage at test point 4 slightly lower than normal, since the balance between the two output transistors TR_2 and TR_3 is no longer produced by the charge on capacitor C_2.

Answer: C_2 o/c.

5.   Bistable multivibrator

(Refer to Fig. 37.13). Normal readings are as follows.

Fig. 37.13

Test point	1	2	3	4	5
State I (TR_1 off)	1.1	0.45	18.5	1.3	1.2
State II (TR_1 on)	1.1	1.3	1.2	0.45	18.5

In each of the following cases the output fails to change when an input pulse is received.

Test point	1	2	3	4	5
Fault A	0.95	0.95	18.5	1.6	1.0
Fault B	0.95	0	18.5	1.6	1.0
Fault C	0.1	0.7	0.1	0.05	18.5
Fault D	1.1	0.45	18.5	1.3	1.2
Fault E	7.7	8.0	19.0	8.0	19.0

Note The bistable has two normal states in which it may settle, hence two normal sets of readings. When locating a fault, first determine the state of each transistor, then compare the faulty readings with the normal readings to determine the reason for the failure to change over from one state to another.

FAULT A

TR_1 off, TR_2 on. TR_1 b−e voltage is zero suggesting a short circuit between base and emitter. Voltage at test point 1 (0.95 V) is now reduced due to the shunting effect of R_4 upon R_3.

Answer: TR_1 b−e s/c.

FAULT B

TR_1 off, TR_2 on. TR_1 base voltage is zero suggesting a faulty bias chain $R_6−R_3$.

Answer: R_6 o/c.

FAULT C

TR_2 is cut off. TR_1 seems saturated; however the low emitter voltage (test point 1 at 0.1 V) indicates cut-off due to open circuit collector resistor R_1. TR_1 collector voltage reading (test point 3) is due to meter resistance. Emitter voltage reading (test point 1) is due to a large base current flowing through forward biased b−e junction of TR_1.

Answer: R_1 o/c.

FAULT D

D.C. readings are normal. Hence fault is a.c.

Answer: C_1 o/c.

FAULT E

The readings are symmetrical with both TR_1 and TR_2 at cut-off. Hence the fault must be common to both transistors. R_4 is the only common component that affects the d.c. conditions of the circuit. Reading at test point 1 is due to meter resistance.

Answer: R_4 o/c.

6. Digital circuit

(Refer to Fig. 37.14)

Output functions of IC5			
C	B	A	Function
0	0	0	Amber
0	0	1	Red
0	1	0	Red
0	1	1	Red/amber
1	0	0	Green

Fig. 37.14

Circuit description: the circuit in Fig. 37.14 shows part of a traffic light controller. Pulses applied at the input are counted by the binary counter IC5, which divides the input by a factor of 5 as shown in the output functions table. The three outputs of IC5, namely C (pin 8), B (pin 9) and A (pin 12) form a binary code for each function of the traffic light system. For instance, when IC5 output CBA are 000 then the Amber light is on, and the Green and Red are off, and for an output of 011 then both Amber and Red are on and the Green is off, and so on. The counter resets itself to 000 after Green. The combinational gates following the counter form a steering circuitry which ensures the correct LED or LEDs are activated. IC7a, b and c are driver amplifiers.

From the following symptom and readings, state the possible fault.

SYMPTOM: NO GREEN

The following logic states were observed on the respective nodes when the circuit was taken through its function by applying individual pulses at the input using a pulser. All readings are observed using a logic probe.

	IC5			IC6d			IC7c	
Pins	C	B	A	4	5	6	3	4
	0	0	0	0	1	1	1	1
	0	0	1	0	1	1	1	1
	0	1	0	0	1	1	1	1
	0	1	1	0	1	1	1	1
	0	0	0	0	1	1	1	1
	0	0	1	0	1	1	1	1

Answer: From the outputs of IC5 it can be seen that the Green sequence (100) is missing, hence IC7c pins 3 and 4 are at logic 1, keeping Green led off. The fault is output C of IC5 stuck-at-0. The counter thus resets itself to 000 immediately after the Red/Amber sequence.
Suspected fault: IC5 pin 8 or pin 2 stuck-at-0.

Component testing

Testing of components is normally carried out by the use of an ohmmeter. The resistance of the component is measured and compared with that of a sound component.

Resistors and inductors

The resistance of a resistor or of an inductor may be measured accurately, thereby giving an indication of a possible fault. Resistors tend to increase their resistance or go open circuit. They very seldom go short circuit. Inductors (and transformers) go open circuit which is easy to detect. They may also develop a shorted turn (i.e. a short circuit between turns) which is fairly common but difficult to detect by ohmmeter measurements, or may develop a short circuit between coil and core which is easy to confirm.

Capacitors

A capacitor may go open circuit, short circuit or leaky. A short circuit or a leak (i.e. a low resistance reading) can easily be detected by ohmmeter measurement. On the other hand it is more difficult to confirm an open-circuit fault. When the ohmmeter terminals are connected across a capacitor, the ohmmeter battery voltage begins to charge up the capacitor. Provided the capacitor has a large value the meter may be observed to kick towards the zero reading and, as the capacitor charges up, its reading slowly rises to infinity. Failure to do that indicates an open circuit. However, a small capacitor would charge up too quickly for the meter to register the movement.

Electrolytic capacitors may be tested for an open circuit because of their high capacitance as well as their normally high leakage current which gives a low resistance reading (few 100 kΩ) when connected in the correct polarity.

Capacitors may change their value, in which case a bridge test where the value of the capacitance is measured is required to detect the fault.

Diodes

The testing of semiconductor devices normally involves the measurement of the forward and reverse resistance of a pn junction. For a diode the ohmmeter is first connected as shown in Fig. 37.15a with a negative terminal connected to the anode, and the positive terminal connected to the cathode. The diode is, therefore, reverse biased giving a very high reading (in MΩ). The polarity is then reversed as shown in Fig. 37.15b giving a forward bias to the diode. A low forward resistance will be registered on the meter (600−1000 Ω on a moving coil, and few ohms on an EVM or DVM). A diode giving a low reading in both directions may be assumed to be a short circuit.

Fig. 37.15 Testing a diode

The ohmmeter test may also be used to identify the anode and cathode terminals of a diode. When the ohmmeter is reading low resistance (i.e. forward biased), as shown in Fig. 37.15b, the polarity of the ohmmeter is the same as the polarity of the diode, i.e. the positive (black) terminal is connected to the anode and the negative (red) terminal is connected to the cathode.

Bipolar transistors

The bipolar transistor consists of two pn junctions which are tested individually in the same way as a diode junction. The forward and reverse resistance of the b−e and b−c junctions are measured separately. Normal readings are of the same order as for an ordinary diode. The resistance between the collector and the emitter is also tested and should give a very high reading (in MΩ) or infinity in both directions.

Junction fet

The ohmmeter is used to measure the resistance of both junctions as well as the channel path itself. For a sound jet the following readings should be obtained:

Drain-gate (forward bias) – low (40 Ω).
Drain-gate (reverse bias) – infinity (MΩ).
Gate-source (forward bias) – low (40 Ω).
Gate-source (reverse bias) – infinity (MΩ).
Drain-source or channel resistance (in either direction) – low (100 Ω).

The SCR

Both the forward and reverse resistances between the anode and the cathode are very high. Triggering may be obtained by connecting the ohmmeter to forward bias the SCR as shown in Fig. 37.16. If the gate is now shorted to the anode, gate current flows which triggers the SCR and makes it conduct. The ohmmeter reading thus drops to a low value (few 100 Ω). The ohmmeter reading remains at that low value even if the shorting link is removed.

Fig. 37.16 Testing an SCR

In-circuit testing

It is always advisable to check a suspected faulty component while it remains in the circuit. Once the fault is confirmed then a replacement may be made. These tests are carried out with the aid of an ohmmeter and usually referred to as *continuity tests*. In carrying out in-circuit measurements, precautions have to be taken to ensure that the shunting effect of other components is minimised or taken into account.

In-circuit measurement of resistance

Consider the circuit in Fig. 37.17 where R_x is the suspected component. An ohmmeter connected across R_x would read the total resistance across A and B. Also $R_1 + R_2 = 10$ kΩ $+ 10$ kΩ $= 20$ kΩ offers a parallel path for the ohmmeter current to flow giving a lower reading on the meter. If R_x is sound, the ohmmeter reading would be

$$\frac{10 \times 20}{10 + 20} = \frac{200}{30} = 6.67 \text{ k}\Omega$$

If R_x is open circuit, the ohmmeter would measure the shunting resistance only, namely 20 kΩ.

The circuit in Fig. 37.17 has a parallel path resistance which is comparable to the resistance of the component under test. Hence

Fig. 37.17 Shunting effect of in-circuit measurement of a resistance

Fig. 37.18 Shunting effect of in-circuit measurement of a resistance

Fig. 37.19 Shunting effect of in-circuit measurement of a resistance

its effect has to be allowed for. In Fig. 37.18, $R_x = 220\ \Omega$. The shunting resistance is $10\ k\Omega + 10\ k\Omega = 20\ k\Omega$ which is 100 times greater than the component under test. In this case the effect of the shunting path may be neglected.

In cases where the suspect component has a value far greater than the total resistance of the shunting path (Fig. 37.19), an in-circuit test becomes unreliable. The ohmmeter gives a reading approximately equal to the total resistance of the shunting path. For the circuit in Fig. 37.19.

$$\text{Meter reading} = \frac{100 \times 20}{100 + 20} = \frac{2000}{120} = 19\ k\Omega$$

Note that a sound component always registers a reading equal to or smaller (due to the shunting path) than its real value and never a higher reading. If a higher reading *is* registered, then the component has gone either high or open circuit.

In many cases a shunting path may include a pn junction either in the form of a diode or a b−e or a b−c junction of a transistor. Figure 37.20 shows a simple single-stage transistor amplifier. To test resistor R_2 assume that the ohmmeter is connected with its positive terminal to the base and its negative terminal to chassis.

Fig. 37.20 Shunting effect of in-circuit measurement of a resistance

    (a)   (b)

The b−e junction becomes forward biased by the ohmmeter battery providing a low resistance shunting path through R_4 as shown in Fig. 37.20a and giving an unreliable reading. If on the other hand the terminals are reversed with the negative connected to the base and the positive to chassis as shown in Fig. 37.20b, the b−e junction becomes reverse biased. The shunting path now consists of a very high reverse resistance of the b−e junction (over $500\ k\Omega$) in series with R_4. The effect of such a high resistance shunting path is of course negligible.

In general therefore when measuring a resistance in-circuit, the ohmmeter terminals must be connected in such a way as to reverse bias any pn junction that may form part of a parallel path in order to minimise the shunting effect. In practice two separate ohmmeter readings are taken with the ohmmeter terminals connected in both directions. *The higher reading is always the more accurate reading*.

Inductors

Inductors (or transformers) have very small resistances. Hence only a very low resistance shunting path has any noticeable effect on the accuracy of the ohmmeter reading.

Capacitors

Leakage may be confirmed by in-circuit ohmmeter measurement test only if the resistance of the shunting path is calculated reasonably accurately. In testing an electrolytic capacitor care must be taken to ensure that the ohmmeter terminals are connected to provide the right polarity to the capacitor.

Diodes and transistors

In testing a suspected diode or a transistor the forward and reverse resistances of the junctions are measured. In the forward direction the resistance of the junction is low, hence the effect of the shunting path is very small. For example, the forward resistance reading of the b−c junction of the transistor in Fig. 37.20 is approximately 400 Ω. In the reverse direction the resistance is very high with the ohmmeter reading mainly the resistance of the shunting path. For the reverse resistance of the b−c junction of the transistor in Fig. 37.20, the ohmmeter reading will be approximately $R_3 + R_1 = 3.3$ kΩ $+ 15$ kΩ $= 17.8$ kΩ.

Note that for an open circuit junction, both the forward and reverse readings will be the same (17.8 kΩ for an open circuit b−c junction in Fig. 37.20).

Fault finding using an ohmmeter

An example is given in Fig. 37.21. The polarity signs given in brackets indicate the polarity of the ohmmeter leads connected to that particular test point. The slider on the potentiometer RV_1 is set to its mid-position.

Fig. 37.21

Fault A   1(+) and 2(−) ≃ 10 kΩ
           1(−) and 2(+) ≃ 10 kΩ
           3(+) and 2(−) ≃ 8.1 kΩ
           3(−) and 2(+) ≃ 8.1 kΩ
           5(+) and 2(−) ≃ 8.9 kΩ
           5(−) and 2(+) = ∞

Fault B   1(+) and 2(−) ≃ 10 kΩ
           1(−) and 2(+) ≃ 2.8 kΩ
           4(+) and 2(−) ≃ 220 Ω
           4(−) and 2(+) ≃ 180 Ω

Fault C   1(+) and 2(−) ≃ 270 kΩ
           1(−) and 2(+) ≃ 3.9 kΩ
           3(+) and 2(−) ≃ 273 kΩ
           3(−) and 2(+) ≃ 1.4 kΩ
           4(+) and 1(−) ≃ 4 kΩ
           4(−) and 1(+) ≃ 270 kΩ

Note Take each reading in turn and compare it with a roughly estimated normal resistance taking account of shunting paths, forward and reverse pn junctions, etc. By a process of elimination one component will be found faulty.

FAULT A

With ohmmeter connected to 1(+) and 2(−), D_1 and D_2 are reverse biased and a reading of 10 kΩ is normal. Reversing the connection, D_1 and D_2 become forward biased. A lower resistance reading would be expected. Since in both cases the ohmmeter gives the same reading, one of the diodes must be open circuit. When the ohmmeter is connected across 5(+) and 2(−), it forward biases D_1 and reverse biases D_2 and gives a normal reading. Reversing the connections the ohmmeter should register a resistance of approximately 700 Ω due to forward biased D_2. An infinite reading indicates a faulty D_2.

Answer: D_2 o/c.

FAULT B

Reading across 1(+) and 2(−) is normal. Reversing the connection, forward biases both diodes. The normal reading is approx. 3.6 kΩ. However the reading on the ohmmeter is lower (2.8 kΩ) indicating the introduction of a shunting resistance when one or both diodes are forward biases both diodes. The normal reading is approximately 3.6 kΩ. the same reading since C_2 remains open-circuit. A lower reading indicates a short-circuited C_2 in which case D_1 is forward biased introducing a shunt across R_3.

Answer: C_2 s/c.

FAULT C

Reading across 1(+) and 2(−) is very high indicating a fault in the main path $RV_1 - R_1$ with the meter reading the high resistance of the shunting path $R_2 - R_3$. With the ohmmeter reversed, D_1 and D_2 are forward biased giving a reading only slightly higher than normal. This confirms that the fault is before D_1. Reading across 3(+) and 2(−) is high (273 kΩ) indicating that the top part of RV_1 is sound. Hence lower half of RV_1 or R_1 is o/c. Remaining tests only confirm this conclusion.

Answer: Lower half of RV_1 o/c or R_1 o/c.

A1 Types of Resistor

Type	Power rating	Stability	Tolerance	Other points
Wire-wound	High (up to 300 W)	High (1%)	5%	Large size Expensive
Carbon	Low (up to 3 W)	Low (20%)	5–20%	Cheap Small size Widely used
Metal or oxide film (precision)	Low (less than 2 W)	High (1%)	Very close	Expensive Small size
Metal or oxide film (power)	High (up to 300 W)	High (1%)	Close	Large size Expensive

A2 Types of Capacitor

Type	Capacitance range	Frequency range	Other points
Paper	0.001−1 μF	Medium (50 Hz−1 MHz)	Cheap
Polystyrene	0.0001−1 μF	Medium	Medium stability (1−5%)
Ceramic	up to few μF	v.h.f. and u.h.f.	Small size High stability
Mica and silver mica	a few pF to 0.05 μF	r.f. (200 MHz or over)	Small size Robust High stability Expensive
Air	very low (up to 0.0005 μF)	v.h.f. and u.h.f.	Bulky Widely used as variable tuning capacitors
Electrolytic	high (up to 1000s μF)	Low (d.c. to a.f.)	Cheap Very high tolerance (over 50%) Widely used

A3 List of SI Units

Angle	radians
Angular velocity	rad/s
Capacitance	farad F
Charge	coulomb C
Current	ampere A
Electromotive force or electric potential	volt V
Energy	joule J
Force	newton N
Frequency	hertz Hz
Impedance	ohm Ω
Inductance	henry H
Length or distance	metre m
Magnetic flux	weber Wb
Magnetic flux density	tesla T
Mass	kilogramme kg
Power	watt W
Pressure	N/m^2
Reactance	ohm Ω
Resistance	ohm Ω
Time	second s
Torque	newton-metre Nm
Velocity or speed	m/s
Weight	newton N
Work	joule J

A4 Component symbols

RESISTORS

Variable resistor   *Preset resistor*   *Potential divider*
(potentiometer)

Thermistor: resistance varies with temperature; usually has a negative temperature coefficient; used to compensate change in resistor values due to change in temperature (e.g. car radios).

*Negative temperature
coefficient resistor*
(e.g. carbon resistors)

*Positive temperature
coefficient (PTC) resistor*
(e.g. wire wound resistor)

Voltage dependent resistor (VDR): maintains a constant voltage across it as current increases

INDUCTORS

General   *Inductor with
magnetic core*   *Variable
inductor*   *Preset
inductor*

TRANSFORMERS

General symbol
(a step-up transformer
having a turns
ratio of 1:2)

*Transformer with
magnetic core*
(a step-down
transformer
having a turns
ratio of 5:1)

*Transformer with
two secondary outputs*
(a turns ratio of
1:5 between
primary and each
secondary)

1:2   5:1   1:5+5

CAPACITORS

Electrolytic capacitor	*Variable capacitor*	*Preset capacitor* or trimmer	*Voltage dependent capacitor*	*Temperature dependent capacitor* (e.g. ceramic)

SEMICONDUCTOR DIODES

General symbol	*Photo diode* (sensitive to light rays)	*Zener diode* (always used at its reverse breakdown voltage which remains constant at all currents; used for voltage stabilization)

THYRISTORS

General symbol
The gate controls the
voltage at which current
can begin to flow from
anode to cathode

*Silicon controlled
rectifier* (SCR)

TRANSISTORS

pnp transistor	*npn transistor*	*Photo-transistor*

OTHER DEVICES

Varactor The variable
capacitor diode presents
a capacitance which
varies with the amount
of reverse bias applied

Field effect   *transistors*

Diac   Triac   Unijunction

Base 1

Base 2

Gate   Emitter

Appendix I
Notes on Calculations

Percentages

A percentage figure is the numerator of a fraction whose denominator is always 100. For example $47\% = \frac{47}{100}$

(1) 5% of $100 = \frac{5}{100} \times 100 = 5$

(2) 10% of 20 V $= \frac{10}{100} \times 20 = 2$ V

(3) A 10 kΩ resistor has a tolerance of $\pm 10\%$. State the maximum and the minimum values that it can have.

10% of 10 kΩ $= \frac{10}{100} \times 100 = 1$ kΩ

Maximum value $= 10 + 1 = 11$ kΩ
Minimum value $= 10 - 1 = 9$ kΩ

Squares and square roots

When a number is multiplied by itself, it is said to be squared. For example $2 \times 2 = 2^2$ (two 'squared') which is equal to 4. We say that 4 is the square of 2. The number of times that the number is multiplied by itself is referred to as the power − in this case 2. In the reverse process, we say that 2 is the square root of 4 or $2 = \sqrt{4}$.

Other powers

The cube of 2 is $2^3 = 2 \times 2 \times 2 = 8$.   5 to the fourth power is $5^4 = 5 \times 5 \times 5 \times 5 = 625$.

Negative powers

General rule: $a^{-2} = \dfrac{1}{a^2}$, $a^{-3} = \dfrac{1}{a^3}$, etc. $3^{-2} = \dfrac{1}{3^2} = \dfrac{1}{9}$

Negative powers change sign (to positive) when moved from the numerator to the denominator, and vice versa.

$$2^{-3} = \frac{1}{2^3} = \frac{1}{8} \qquad \frac{1}{3^{-2}} = 3^2 = 9$$

Any number lifted to the power of zero is equal to one: $2^0 = 1$, $10^0 = 1$.

Powers of ten

An easy way of dealing with calculations involving many decimal points is the use of the powers of ten.

$$10^0 = \qquad 1 \qquad 10^{-1} = \frac{1}{10} = 0.1$$

$$10^1 = \qquad 10 \qquad 10^{-2} = \frac{1}{100} = 0.01$$

$$10^2 = \qquad 100 \qquad 10^{-3} = \frac{1}{1000} = 0.001$$

$$10^3 = \qquad 1\ 000 \qquad 10^{-4} = \frac{1}{10\ 000} = 0.0001$$

$$10^4 = \qquad 10\ 000 \qquad 10^{-5} = \frac{1}{100\ 000} = 0.000\ 01$$

$$10^5 = \qquad 100\ 000 \qquad 10^{-6} = \frac{1}{1\ 000\ 000} = 0.000\ 001$$

$$10^6 = 1\ 000\ 000$$

For example, $2000\ V = 2 \times 1000\ V = 2 \times 10^3\ V$ and $0.01\ A = 10^{-2}\ A$.

In multiplying, powers of ten are added:

$$10^2 \times 10^1 = 10^{2+1} = 10^3 \quad 10^4 \times 10^{-1} = 10^{4-1} = 10^3$$

Multiples and sub-multiples of units

Multiplication factor		Prefix	Symbol
1 000 000 000	10^9	Giga	G
1 000 000	10^6	Mega	M
1 000	10^3	kilo	k
0.001	10^{-3}	milli	m
0.000 001	10^{-6}	micro	μ
0.000 000 001	10^{-9}	nano	n
0.000 000 000 001	10^{-12}	pico	p

EXAMPLE 1

If the current through a 4.7 kΩ resistor is 2 mA, what would be the voltage drop across the resistor?

$4.7 \text{ k}\Omega = 4.7 \times 10^3 \Omega$ and $2 \text{ mA} = 3 \times 10^{-3}$ A
$V = IR = 2 \times 10^{-3} \times 4.7 \times 10^3 = 2 \times 4.7 \times 10^{-3} \times 10^3$
$= 2 \times 4.7 \times 10^0 = 2 \times 4.7 \times 1 = 2 \times 4.7 = 9.4$ V

Appendix II
The Decibel

The decibel (dB) is a logarithmic unit for expressing the ratio of two powers, such as power gain. The decibel is a more suitable unit to use than the numerical gain ratio because it provides a smaller number for the gain. It is also more convenient to use in a.f. applications because the human ear responds to sound intensities in a logarithmic manner.

For the amplifier shown in Fig. A.1 where p_{in} and p_o are the input and output powers, the power gain G_p in dB is given as

Fig. A.1

$$G_p = 10 \log_{10} \frac{\text{Output power}}{\text{Input power}} = 10 \log_{10} \frac{p_o}{p_{in}} \text{ dB}$$

Since p_o/p_{in} = power gain, then
gain in dB = $10 \log_{10}$ (power gain).

It should be noted that the decibel is a unit of power ratio and not a measure of the power level.

The gain in dB may be either positive or negative. A positive dB value represents a gain ratio greater than 1 (p_o greater than p_{in}), while a negative dB value represents a gain ratio smaller than 1 (p_o smaller than p_{in} i.e. a *loss*).

To calculate the gain in dB using the formula given above requires a knowledge of logarithms. It is therefore useful to memorise the basic conversions given in Table A.1 which, as we shall see later, may be used to calculate most of the conversions that are likely to crop up.

It should be noted that (*a*) for a gain of 1 the dB gain is zero and

Table A.1

dB gain	Power gain
0	1
3	2
10	10
20	100 (10^2)
30	1000 (10^3)

Table A.2

dB gain	Voltage or* current gain
0	1
3	$\sqrt{2} = 1.4$
6	2
20	10
40	100
60	1000

(*b*) that a 10 times increase in gain (e.g. from 100 to 1000) the dB gain increases by 10 dB (from 20 to 30). For a loss, the dB value is negative. For example, a gain of $\frac{1}{2} = -3$ dB and $1/10 = -10$ dB and so on.

EXAMPLES

(1) If an amplifier has a gain of 3 dB, and an input of 10 mW then the output may be calculated as follows:

$$3\text{ dB} = \text{a power gain of } 2$$

Hence, Output $= 2 \times$ input $= 2 \times 10$ mW $= 20$ mW

(2) Refer to Fig. A.2. To find the input power:

$$10\text{ dB} = \text{a power gain of } 10$$

Hence, Input power $= \dfrac{\text{Output power}}{10} = \dfrac{100\text{ mW}}{10} = 10$ mW

Gain = 10 dB   100 mW

Fig. A.2

Voltage and current gains

Both voltage and current gains of a circuit can be calculated in decibels, *provided* the input and load resistances are of *equal* value, as follows:

$$\text{Gain in dB} = 20 \log \frac{v_o}{v_{in}} = 20 \log \frac{i_o}{i_{in}}$$

where v_o and i_o are the output, and v_{in} and i_{in} are the input voltage and current respectively.

* Table A.2 assumes equal resistances.

From Table A.2 -3 dB $=$ a voltage gain of $1/1.4 = 0.7$ or 70%. For example, if a 3 dB attenuator (i.e. having a dB loss of 3 dB) has an input voltage of 10 mV then the output is $0.7 \times 10 = 7$ mV.

Fig. A.3

Fig. A.4

Multi-stage gain

One further advantage of using decibels is that the gain in dB of an amplifier having more than one stage is equal to the sum of the dB gain of each stage. Fig. A.3 shows a two-stage amplifier. Stage 1 has a gain of 10 dB (i.e. a power gain of 10) and stage 2 has a gain of 3 dB (or a power gain of 2). The overall gain is 10 dB + 3 dB = 13 dB. The overall power gain ratio on the other hand is given as the product of the gain of each stage, namely 10 × 2 = 20.

EXAMPLE Refer to Fig. A.4.

Stage A gain = 100/10 = 10, or 20 dB (Assuming $R_{in} = R_L$)
Stage B gain = 70/100 = 0.7, or −3 dB.
Overall gain = 70/10 = 7. Overall gain in dB = 20 − 3
                                                          = 17 dB.

Conversion from decibels to ratios or vice versa for values other than those given in the two tables may be worked out by subdivision into suitable stages. For example, 13 dB may be divided into 10 dB + 3 dB, and 10 dB is a ratio of 10 and 3 dB is a ratio of 2. Hence the total equivalent ratio is 10 × 2 = 20 (refer to Fig. A.3).

EXAMPLES

(3) If the input to a device is 10 mW and its output is 1 W what is the gain in dB?

Solution

$$\text{Power gain} = \frac{1 \text{ W}}{10 \text{ mW}} = \frac{1000 \text{ mW}}{10 \text{ mW}} = 100$$

A power gain of 100 = 20 dB.

(4) Refer to Fig. A.5. Find (*a*) the overall gain, (*b*) the overall gain in dB, (*c*) the gain of stage B in dB and as a ratio.

Fig. A.5

Solution

(*a*) Overall gain $= \dfrac{v_o}{v_{in}} = \dfrac{100 \text{ mV}}{50 \text{ mV}} = 2$

(*b*) Voltage gain of 2 = 6 dB.
(*c*) Gain of stage B = 6 dB − 9 dB = −3 dB.
        Stage B gain as a ratio is 1/1.4 = 0.7.

Index